# Canadian Automotive Service Technician

## Certificate of Qualification Test Preparation, Second Edition

**SEAN BENNETT**

**DAVE WEATHERHEAD**

**Centennial College Press**

LIBRARY AND ARCHIVES CANADA CATALOGUING IN PUBLICATION
Bennett, Sean
    Canadian automotive service technician : certificate of qualification
test preparation / Bennett and Weatherhead. — 2nd ed.

First published under title: AST prep certificate of qualification for
Canadian automotive service technicians.
ISBN 978-0-919852-61-7

1. Automobiles—Maintenance and repair—Examinations—Study
guides. 2. Automobiles—Maintenance and repair—Examinations,
questions, etc. I. Weatherhead, Dave. II. Bennett, Sean. AST prep
certificate of qualification for Canadian automotive service technicians.
III. Title.

TL152.B36 2007          629.28'72076          C2007-904634-7

Centennial College Press
951 Carlaw Avenue
Toronto, Ontario
M4K 3M2

Book design and typesetting by Laura Brady

Printed in Canada by Webcom

# Contents ➤

# Introduction to the Second Edition ➤ 1

Red Seal Automotive Service Technician exams are devised by provincially licensed, practising technicians with little input from academics. The Red Seal test preparation workshops are given some guidelines to work with, but on the whole they create questions based on the Federal Occupational Analyses (see Chapter 4) and slot them into the reportable subject categories of the provincial C of Q exams (see Chapter 3). This means that though all Certificate of Qualification exams are made up of Red Seal questions, they are organized by each province's reportable subject categories, which are themselves based on the Training Standards for a given province. As you will see from reading Chapters 3 and 4, the Red Seal and provincial subject groupings are very similar.

This edition presents its questions in the Federal, or Red Seal, format with the Red Seal Blocks (divisions of subjects) used instead of one sample province's reportable subjects, as we did in the previous edition. We also explain in Chapters 3 and 4 how to use your knowledge of your province's reportable subjects to weight your study time for each. Again, although the questions on any C of Q exam are all drawn from the same source, the number of questions in each reportable subject, or weighting for each subject, will differ.

Last, this book presents an entirely new practice test of 125 questions.

## Objectives of the Book

This book is a guide to Canadian Red Seal Certificate of Qualification testing for Automotive Service Technicians. It will not replace the hands-on experience of a 4- or 5-year apprenticeship, the in-school formal theoretical learning period, or textbooks that deal in detail with the subject matter. Our goal is to help students who are in a final preparation phase before writing a Certificate of Qualification exam to understand the type of questions in the test and the relative weighting of the subject matter. This book will be excellent preparation for the exam.

## Reportable Subjects

When preparing to write a C of Q exam, it is very important to closely observe the reportable subject categories so that you have an idea of how many questions you are likely to get on a particular subject area. For instance, if you take a look at Chapter 3 in this book, you will note that the *provincial* reportable subject *Engine Management*

*Systems* has 27 questions dedicated to it, but the subject *Body, Hardware, Trim, and Accessories* has only 6. This means that every Red Seal C of Q written in the province of Ontario will have exactly that number of questions on each of those reportable subjects.

Knowing the number of questions for each reportable subject is important when it comes to studying for a test because it means you can prioritize study time by the weighting—that is, the relative importance of each subject. Knowing that there are 22 questions on *Steering, Suspension and Brake Systems* (heavily weighted), which is 18% of the test, means that you should probably devote roughly 18% of your available study time to this subject. Plan your study time so that you use it as efficiently as possible.

## The Exam Questions

All questions on a Certificate of Qualification exam are sourced from both the Federal Occupational Analyses and the Provincial Training Standards. In practice, every question asked in a C of Q must be justified by these two sources. A profile of one province's Training Standards is included in Chapter 4 of this book, so it would probably benefit you to take a look at them. Provincial Training Standards are the on-the-job requirements of an apprenticeship contract. When you, your employer, and apprenticeship counsellor sign an apprenticeship contract, you are committing to attain competency in each Training Standard task, and your employer is committing to provide the conditions to enable that. More important—let's say it again—C of Q questions are sourced from the Federal Occupational Analyses and Provincial Training Standards, NOT the in-school provincial curriculum you studied in college. It is therefore possible that you will find questions on procedures and technologies that you did not study in the college curriculum. Provincial college curriculum tends to be changed more frequently than the training standards. Changes are recommended by an Industry Committee, and its advice is converted to curriculum by a Curriculum Development Committee consisting mostly of college teachers.

The questions in the tests in this book have been constructed to broadly cover the tasks identified in the Federal Occupational Analyses of the Automotive Service Technician trade to help the student prepare for the Certificate of Qualification. For instance, in Practice Test 1 there is a troubleshooting question on an oxygen sensor which is probably more difficult than anything you would find on a current C of Q. However, the question is designed so that if you fully understand both the question and its response, you should be capable of answering most possible C of Q questions on oxygen sensor malfunctions.

## Using This Book

Finally, this is an exam preparation book, not a comprehensive textbook. It is designed to complement and reinforce knowledge you already have. If you are unable to understand an explanation, you may have to refer to some of the textbooks recommended at the end of the book. If you have completed the required in-school training, you are probably in possession of one of the comprehensive automotive textbooks, and this is all you need. If you have a specific weakness in a subject area, you may benefit from one of the specialty textbooks; these will often go into a technology with a thoroughness well beyond that required for a provincial certification examination.

# Test Strategies  ➤  2

Every student learns differently, so the learning method that works best for one person may not work for another. Generally, you should not leave review and study time to the last moment. Spending 15 minutes a day for 6 months will be more effective for most learners than spending a week before a test studying to the point of exhaustion. Most learners forget material if they do not review the subject matter. Look at the following data produced from testing following a lecture:

| % retained in memory | Without review | With review |
|---|---|---|
| After 24 hours | 60% | 80% |
| After 1 week | 50% | 75% |
| After 2 weeks | 40% | 70% |
| After 3 weeks | 30% | 70% |
| After 4 weeks | 20% | 70% |

National Institute for Staff and Organizational Development

The above chart shows the value of establishing a routine of review. For most learners, reviewing material is a key to succeeding in exams. The great thing about making a review a habit is that it does not take long. If you properly understood the material first time around, minutes are all that is required to refresh the learning experience in your mind. The following is an example of a review timetable that will work for most students.

## Review 1

This should take place within 24 hours of the learning experience. The same day works best for most learners. This review step is the most important in the review process. Use point-form notes—that is, keep notes as brief as possible. When instructors write out notes or issue handouts, abbreviate them. Short-form notes are a great study tool, just make sure that they are not abbreviated to the extent that they cease to have meaning to you. In this first review, try to understand the subject matter. Make notes about material you do not grasp and make it your business to get those questions answered by either private research or your teacher.

## Review 2

Go over your abbreviated notes in this session. Make sure you understand both your own notes and the subject matter covered. This second review should take a matter of minutes. You will be recalling the learning experience and the time you devoted to the first review.

## Review 3

In this step, you simply relive the initial learning experience and the first review step. It should take little time and you may even feel it is boring. However, it is a great way to reinforce the information learned. Depending on what type of learner you are, you may want to do this once a month. But do it, it does work, and the payoff will come when you are tested.

## Review 4

This should be done immediately before testing. Most learners do not retain information well when their only study occurs immediately prior to an exam. Try not to spend too long studying because if you do, your brain will be exhausted by the time you have to challenge the test. One thing that can work well is joining a small study group before a test. Use sets of typical test questions such as those found in this book as a basis for discussion.

## Active Learning

Auto technicians tend to learn best by doing rather than thinking, which is why we often feel out of place in classrooms. Become active in the classroom by using some of the following strategies:

1. *Make your own notes.* Most teachers write far too much on boards and in their handouts, so rewrite what they say in terms that mean something to you. Notes are for you only. Challenge yourself to make them as meaningful as possible. Remember, notes are a great review instrument, especially if you can capture the essence of a 3-hour class in 1 page of bullet-form notes.

2. *Draw diagrams.* Try not to always rely on handouts. Drawing a diagram makes you active in the class. Even if you don't have much artistic ability, the actions required to draw a diagram will usually help you better understand the technology.

3. *Ask questions in class.* That is, ask them if you feel comfortable doing so. Not all automotive technicians like to ask questions in class. But asking questions, even if you think they are dumb questions, is a way of making yourself an active learner, and that helps retention.

4. *Look for ways of making connections between the theoretical information you get in class and the hands-on practice of repair technology.* This works well if you have worked hands-on with the technology you are learning in class.

## Reading Textbooks

Most textbooks are difficult to pick up and read in serial fashion like a novel. When you use a textbook to study, define what your goals are before opening the book and then use the book to meet them. Before you begin, it is a good idea to know something about the goals you want to achieve, so write them down in brief form. Next, you have to navigate the contents of the textbook to achieve those goals. Here is an action plan I use when studying subject matter that is new to me:

1. *Goals.* Define your goals. Write them down on paper. This could be as simple as a couple of words or it could be more complex, depending on what it is you are expecting to learn.

2. *Survey.* You have your goals in note form on paper. Next, consult the textbook's table of contents to determine if the book is going to be of any help. Try to avoid using the index to search for information; indexing does not usually indicate where critical explanations occur in the text. Once you have targeted a chapter in the textbook, take a look at the chapter objectives: this should give you a pretty good idea of whether the chapter is the best to start with.

3. *Read, distill, and restate.* Target the information you need in the text. Read the content and get a general sense of what the author is trying to say. In most cases, what the author is saying can be restated in fewer words. Using pen and paper, take bullet notes on the content. Keep it brief. Most important: put everything in words that make sense to YOU.

4. *Review.* Close the textbook and go over the bullet-form notes you have made. Does it make sense to you? If it does not, you will have to open the book up again and redo the notes. If it does make sense and the notes you have made are sufficient to allow you to recall the material later on, you have achieved your objective.

## Improving Retention 记忆力

Because we all learn differently, remember that what works for you may be different from what works for others. We said before that automotive technicians generally learn best when a learning experience is active. That very often means hands-on learning that is not always possible in college programs with congested curriculum and large classes, so look for other ways of making the learning experience real for you. Here are some key things that might work:

- *Active classroom learning.* Use the classroom techniques we described earlier to avoid being a completely passive participant in the learning process. Because you are more likely to learn by doing, DO as much as possible in class. Condense existing notes, draw diagrams, ask questions.

- *Research information.* Use the Internet if this approach to learning works for you. It is a great way of supplementing what you have learned in the classroom, and the best thing is that you control both the learning path and the pace. Again, make those short bullet-form notes when you are hunting down info online.

- *Use video.* Most colleges have enormous video libraries that are too lengthy to run in structured classes. But if you like to learn visually, use the video, CD, and DVD libraries in resource centers to learn. Most auto manufacturers make good quality CDs and DVDs, some of them interactive, that teach the technology they are using in their vehicles. Note: video is a big turn-off for some and has a way of inducing sleep. If this is true for you, recognize it and avoid long video presentations.

- *Active research.* This can really be effective. In teaching engine technology, it is common to hear students complain that they never work on engines and find it difficult to understand repair techniques. Most technicians should be able to obtain an engine for little or no investment. Take one apart in your garage and reassemble it. It doesn't matter whether it will ever run again, the experience of disassembly/reassembly will stick in your mind forever.

- *Be curious.* This is your career. Don't black box technology. If you do not understand how a particular component functions, get one that has failed, test it with test instruments, and take it apart, with a hacksaw if necessary. Make it your business to answer those questions that no one seems to have an answer for.

## Improving Test-Writing Skills

Most automotive technicians are not academics by inclination and it often seems unfair that they are examined academically rather than by practical tasks. The only province in Canada that uses hands-on testing of motive power technicians is Quebec; however, some provinces offer hands-on testing for technicians that have failed written tests, usually at considerable extra cost. The modern automotive technician must be literate, so attempting to justify a paper examination failure by claiming to have mastered all the hands-on competencies fools no one but yourself. However, there are some simple things you should be aware of that can greatly improve your ability to succeed in tests:

1. *The number one reason for failing a test is simply not knowing the material.* Use the study techniques described in this guide to ensure that you understand the subject matter.

2. *Never spend too much time analyzing a test question.* If you do not understand a question, skip it and return to it when you have completed the questions you do understand. Analyzing is a great skill for a technician—but it can hinder you when writing a test by causing you to read meanings into a test question that are not there.

3. *A typical test question consists of a stem or question followed by 4 possible answers.* Only 1 of the 4 possible answers is correct: the other 3 are known as distractors. When you are not sure of the answer, try eliminating obvious distractors by crossing them out. This will help narrow down your choices.

4. *Read with your pencil.* Underline key words in the question. Eliminate distractors that make no sense at all. If you have to guess, make sure your guess is an intelligent one; you can only do this if you have already eliminated the distractors that do not make sense.

5. *Read the question and* ALL *the answers.* It may be that some of the distractors are in some way correct. In a multiple choice test you are selecting the MOST correct answer.

6. *Distribute your time appropriately.* This is especially important if you know you write tests slowly. Take off your watch and place it above the test paper. Divide the test into sections. Answer those questions you find easy first.

7. *Forget about answer patterns.* If you have answered A for the previous 4 questions, it is of no significance. Certificate of Qualification exams are drawn from computerized test question banks, so there is nothing significant about the correct answer patterns expected in the test.

8. *Think twice before changing an answer in a multiple choice test.* Studies show that more often than not a correct answer is changed to an *incorrect* answer—take a look at point #2 about over-analyzing test questions. The answer that first occurs to you is likely to be correct.

9. *Erasing.* Certificate of Qualification exams are graded optically by scanning. If you erase an answer, make sure that it is completely erased. If not, 2 answers will be scanned on the question and you will get the question wrong. If you are unable to properly erase a response that you feel is incorrect, ask for another answer sheet.

10. *Answer every question.* In a Certificate of Qualification exam there are 4 possible answers for every question and only 1 answer is correct. You do not get penalized for incorrect responses. Even if you are outright guessing the answer, you still have a 25% chance of getting it right!

11. *Relax!* If the test becomes confusing to you, spend 5 minutes daydreaming to get your mind off the test. You may just find that what was confusing you becomes less so. Breathe slowly and deeply if you are inclined to panic during tests.

12. *Don't expect every question in the test to be absolutely technically accurate.* Certificate of Qualification test questions are written by teams of journeyperson technicians, not academics. Despite checks and a proofing procedure, it is possible for the odd question to appear in a test that makes little sense. If you get a question like this, try asking yourself which answer the author of the question might have thought was correct. More important, avoid getting too worked up over one bad question! Move on to the next.

13. *In any question involving personal or shop safety, think about the correct way, not what you might think is accepted practice.*

# Exam Profile ➤ 3
# and Reportable Subjects

---

Canadian Certificate of Qualification examinations in the Motive Power Trades are prepared by the provinces and based on the Federal Occupational Analyses for each specific trade. The Canadian provinces work together, orchestrated by Red Seal, in the construction of the computerized test banks, usually with one province taking the lead responsibility. The responsibility for managing the Red Seal Automotive Service Technician questions at this time rests with the province of Ontario; other provinces provide a similar lead role in the other motive power trades; for instance, the Red Seal Truck and Transport Technician responsibility currently lies with British Columbia.

If you live in a province other than Ontario (not including Quebec), you are likely to write pretty much the same examination as that used in Ontario because the questions are sourced from the same question bank. However, the subject matter WEIGHT-INGS within the test may be different. Subject matter weightings are important because they determine the structure of the exam profile. The exam profile indicates the exact number of questions you will get in each reportable subject.

## Occupational Analysis

The Occupational Analysis looks at the competencies required by an Automotive Service Technician and divides these competencies in the following manner:

**Block**     A block is the largest competency division within the analysis and can be regarded as a major set of skills sharing at least one thing in common. For instance, *Engine Systems* is the title of one of the 7 blocks that compose the AST Occupational Analysis. These 7 blocks are important in the Exam Profile because each identifies a reportable subject for purposes of constructing the Certificate of Qualification.

All Red Seal exams are divided by each province's reportable subjects, all of which are very similar but differ in the exact wording of each subject and in the number of questions each subject has. We present our test questions using the Red Seal's reportable subjects or blocks, to avoid using any specific province's reportable subjects. Just remember to know your province's Training Standards and reportable subjects to learn about how each of your province's reportable subjects may have more or fewer questions than those of the Red Seal.

| Task | A task is a distinct activity that falls under a block of skills. For instance, *Diagnosing Engine Performance* is a set of skills that falls under the *Engine Systems* block. |

**Task** A task is a distinct activity that falls under a block of skills. For instance, *Diagnosing Engine Performance* is a set of skills that falls under the *Engine Systems* block.

**Sub-task** A sub-task is a specific competency or skill that falls under a task. For instance, *Using a Scan Tool* is a specific skill that would be one of many required to achieve competency in the task *Diagnosing Engine Performance.*

## AST Occupational Analysis Blocks

Seven blocks compose the Federal Automotive Service Technician Occupational Analysis. They are as follows:

Block A — Occupational Skills. Tasks: Uses Tools and Equipment; Organizes Work; Performs General Work and Maintenance.

Block B — Engine Systems. Tasks: Diagnoses Engine Systems; Repairs Engine Systems; Diagnoses Engine Support Systems; Repairs Engine Support Systems.

Block C — Vehicle Management Systems. Tasks: Diagnoses Vehicle Management Systems; Repairs Vehicle Management Systems.

Block D — Drive Line Systems. Tasks: Diagnoses Drive Line Systems; Repairs Drive Line Systems.

Block E — Electrical and Comfort Control Systems. Tasks: Diagnoses Electrical Systems and Components; Repairs Electrical Systems and Components; Diagnoses HVAC and Comfort Control; Repairs HVAC and Comfort Control.

Block F — Steering, Suspension, Braking, and Control Systems. Tasks: Diagnoses Steering, Suspension, Braking, and Control Systems; Repairs Steering, Suspension, Braking, and Control Systems.

Block G — Body Components, Trim, and Restraint Systems. Tasks: Diagnoses Body Components, Trim, and Restraint Systems; Repairs Body Components, Trim, and Restraint Systems.

## Analysis of an Exam Profile by Reportables

Within the Certificate of Qualification, the questions are constructed around the Federal Occupational Analysis skill sets we identified above. They are based on these and the Provincial Training Standards. Each province can weight the reportable subjects, though in reality there is little significant difference between one province and another. The following is a Province of Ontario exam profile; note that the title of each reportable subject within the profile is almost identical to the title of the federal skill set block. Each province's reportable subjects are created based upon the practical knowledge areas of that province's Traning Standards.

| Reportable Subject—Block of Tasks | % of Test | # of Questions |
|---|---|---|
| 1. Work Practices and Safety | 7% | 9 |
| 2. Internal Combustion Engines | 14% | 18 |
| 3. Engine Management Systems | 22% | 27 |
| 4. Drive Line Systems | 14% | 18 |
| 5. Electrical, Electronic, and Vacuum Control Systems | 20% | 25 |
| 6. Steering, Suspension, and Brakes | 18% | 22 |
| 7. Body, Hardware, Trim, and Accessories | 5% | 6 |
| **TOTAL** | 100% | **125** |

Both with the Red Seal format and the Ontario format there are 7 categories of reportable subject. Each of these is weighted. The heavier the weighting, the more questions. The weighting does not change from test to test. For instance, if you and a friend go to write your C of Q on the same day, you will not necessarily write exactly the same questions because they are drawn at random from a question bank. But you will both write exactly 6 questions relating to the *Body, Hardware, Trim, and Accessories* category of questions. So, in preparing to write your C of Q, take a very close look at the weighting of each category of Training Standard. This will help you strategize your study time. If you check the chart below, you will notice that there are 27 questions on *Engine Management Systems* and only 6 on *Body, Hardware, Trim, and Accessories*. So, it is obvious that you should dedicate more time to the study of *Engine Management Systems* when prepping for your test.

## Emphasis on Training Standards in the C of Q Exam

Most apprentices eligible to write a Canadian Red Seal Certificate of Qualification will have attended the in-school training sessions delivered by provincial colleges and managed by provincial education authorities. The formal curriculum used in the in-school portion of apprenticeship training is designed to complement the content of the Training Standards. In most cases, the formal in-school curriculum is driven by a Provincial Industry Committee made up of an Original Equipment Manufacturer (OEM), large dealer, small dealer, and independent representatives, and it usually covers a much broader spectrum than the Training Standards. For instance, theoretical knowledge is a key building block to any technical skill set, so the curriculum emphasizes plenty of theory en route to achieving competency. But remember this: **the provincial test you are going to write is based not on the curriculum you studied in your college program but directly on the Federal Occupational Analysis and Provincial Training Standards. Remember this too: the Certificate of Qualification exam attempts to make a determination of your *competence* in each reportable task**. This means that you should not see questions that are purely theoretical. Each question is going to have a practical—that is, applied—motif. This does not mean you do not have to know any theory, but it does mean you will be unlikely to see a question like this typical in-school example:

*What happens chemically to the ozone layer when chlorine base refrigerant is released into the atmosphere?* (Answer: chlorine dioxide leaches an oxygen atom from the ozone molecule [$O_3$] reducing it to $O_2$.)

You will see this type of question in tests when you study air-conditioning systems in college because in the curriculum there is a clear mandate to look at technology from both a theoretical and a practical point of view.

In a Red Seal C of Q, you are more likely to see something like this:

*Which of the following would likely result from a slightly low charge of refrigerant in a CCOT A/C system?*
   A. Compressor damage.
   B. Higher than normal gauge readings.
   C. Noisier compressor operation.
   D. More frequent than normal clutch cycling.

**The correct answer is D.**

In this question, your knowledge of an on-the-job procedure is being tested rather than your academic competency with theoretical concepts.

One thing that cannot be emphasized strongly enough when strategizing your study preparation is the importance of understanding the role of college in-school training and that of workplace training. **In terms of total apprenticeship time, typically 10% is spent in formal in-school instruction while 90% is on the job.** Not everything you need to know is going to be learned in the in-school portion of apprenticeship. On-the-job training is fundamental to apprenticeship; in fact, it is what makes it effective. So expect questions that test your on-the-job knowledge of service procedures and diagnosis.

## Key Points

- Test questions relate to Training Standards and are application-based. Expect lots of questions that relate to hands-on procedures.

- Strategize your exam preparation by looking at the number of questions dedicated to each reportable subject category for your province's Training Standard, 7 in all.

- Apprenticeship consists of approximately 10% in-school training and 90% on-the-job training. The Certificate of Qualification is designed to determine your on-the-job competence, not just the more theoretical knowledge you learned in the college curriculum.

# Sample Provincial Training Standards: Ontario

In most provinces, you are issued a Training Standards booklet when you sign an apprenticeship contract. Your supervisor is expected to sign off on each of the Training Standards as you progress through the apprenticeship term. As we have said many times, it is important to note that the Red Seal Certificate of Qualification exam is based on the Federal Occupational Analysis and Provincial Training Standards and NOT the in-school curriculum you followed during your time in college. It makes sense that you should make yourself familiar with the Training Standards because they identify the skill sets in more detail than you will find them in the Federal Occupational Analysis. Further, they will help you refocus your study on the hands-on knowledge you gained during your on-the-job training, which most of the exam questions are based upon.

This section lists the Automotive Service Technician Training Standards used in Ontario. You will find something very similar in each of the other provinces.

## AST TRAINING STANDARDS

### SECTION 5160, OCCUPATIONAL HEALTH & SAFETY PRACTICES

1. 5160.01—Identify Potential Workplace Health and Safety Hazards
2. 5160.02—Handle, Store and Dispose of Hazardous Materials
3. 5160.03—Wear and Maintain Personal Protective Equipment
4. 5160.04—Comply with Workplace Related Legislation
5. 5160.05—Interpret and Apply Service Related Information
6. 5160.06—Practice Good Housekeeping in the Workplace
7. 5160.07—Comply with WHMIS Guidelines

### SECTION 5161, ENGINE SYSTEMS

1. 5161.01—Perform Visual Inspection
2. 5161.02—Diagnose and Troubleshoot Cooling Systems and Components
3. 5161.03—Repair Cooling Systems and Components
4. 5161.04—Verify Repair of Cooling Systems and Components
5. 5161.05—Diagnose and Troubleshoot Engine Lubricating Systems and Components
6. 5161.06—Repair Engine Lubricating Systems and Components
7. 5161.07—Verify Repair of Engine Lubricating Systems and Components

8.  5161.08—Diagnose Cylinder Head and Components
9.  5161.09—Repair Cylinder Head and Components
10. 5161.10—Verify Repair of Cylinder Head and Components
11. 5161.11—Diagnose and Troubleshoot Engine Block and Components
12. 5161.12—Repair Engine Block and Components
13. 5161.13—Verify Repair of Engine Block and Components

## SECTION 5162, ELECTRICAL SYSTEMS: STARTING AND CHARGING

1.  5162.01—Perform Visual Inspection
2.  5162.02—Diagnose and Troubleshoot Batteries
3.  5162.03—Service and Boost/Charge Batteries
4.  5162.04—Diagnose and Troubleshoot Starting Systems and Components
5.  5162.05—Repair Starting Systems and Components
6.  5162.06—Verify Repair of Starting Systems and Components
7.  5162.07—Diagnose and Troubleshoot Charging Systems and Components
8.  5162.08—Repair Charging Systems and Components
9.  5162.09—Verify Repair of Charging Systems and Components

## SECTION 5163, ENGINE MANAGEMENT SYSTEMS

1.  5163.01—Perform Visual Inspection
2.  5163.02—Diagnose and Troubleshoot Fuel Control Systems and Components
3.  5163.03—Repair Fuel Control Systems and Components
4.  5163.04—Diagnose and Troubleshoot Ignition Systems and Components
5.  5163.05—Repair Ignition Systems and Components
6.  5163.06—Diagnose and Troubleshoot Computer-Controlled Systems
7.  5163.07—Repair Computer-Controlled Systems and Components
8.  5163.08—Perform Gasoline Engine Tune-Ups
9.  5163.09—Perform Electronic Diesel Engine Tune-Ups
10. 5163.10—Perform Mechanical Diesel Engine Tune-Ups

## SECTION 5164, ELECTRICAL SYSTEMS: BODY

1.  5164.01—Perform Visual Inspection
2.  5164.02—Diagnose and Troubleshoot Body Electrical and Computer-Controlled Systems and Components
3.  5164.03—Repair Body Electrical and Computer-Controlled Systems and Components
4.  5164.04—Verify Repair of Body Electrical and Computer-Controlled Systems and Components
5.  5164.05—Diagnose and Troubleshoot Supplemental Restraint Systems and Components
6.  5164.06—Repair Supplemental Restraint Systems and Components
7.  5164.07—Verify and Test Seat Belt Assembly

## SECTION 5165, FUEL DELIVERY SYSTEMS

1.  5165.01—Perform Visual Inspection
2.  5165.02—Diagnose and Troubleshoot Gasoline Fuel Systems and Components
3.  5165.03—Diagnose and Repair Gasoline Fuel Systems and Components

4. 5165.04—Verify Repair of Gasoline Fuel Systems and Components
5. 5165.05—Diagnose and Troubleshoot Diesel Fuel Systems and Components
6. 5165.06—Repair Diesel Fuel Systems and Components
7. 5165.07—Verify Repair of Diesel Fuel Systems and Components

## SECTION 5166, TRANSMISSIONS AND CLUTCHES

1. 5166.01—Perform Visual Inspection
2. 5166.02—Diagnose and Troubleshoot Clutch Systems and Components
3. 5166.03—Repair Clutch Systems and Components
4. 5166.04—Verify Repair of Clutch Systems and Components
5. 5166.05—Diagnose and Troubleshoot Transmission/Transaxle and Components
6. 5166.06—Repair Transmission/Transaxle and Components
7. 5166.07—Verify Repair of Manual Transmission/Transaxle and Components
8. 5166.08—Diagnose and Troubleshoot Automatic Transmission/Transaxle and Components
9. 5166.09—Repair Automatic Transmission/Transaxle and Components
10. 5166.10—Verify Repair of Automatic Transmission/Transaxle and Components
11. 5166.11—Repair Computer-Controlled Systems and Components
12. 5166.12—Verify Repair of Computer-Controlled Systems and Components
13. 5166.13—Diagnose and Troubleshoot Transfer Case and Components
14. 5166.14—Repair Transfer Case and Components
15. 5166.15—Verify Repair of Transfer Case and Components

## SECTION 5167, DRIVE SHAFTS, DIFFERENTIALS AND DRIVE AXLE ASSEMBLIES

1. 5167.01—Perform Visual Inspection
2. 5167.02—Diagnose and Troubleshoot Drive Shafts, Differentials, Drive Axle Assemblies and Components
3. 5167.03—Repair Drive Shafts, Differentials, Drive Axle Assemblies and Components
4. 5167.04—Verify Repair of Drive Shafts, Differentials, Drive Axle Assemblies and Components

## SECTION 5168, SUSPENSION SYSTEMS AND FRAMES

1. 5168.01—Perform Visual Inspection
2. 5168.02—Diagnose and Troubleshoot Suspension Systems, Frames/Sub Frames and Components
3. 5168.03—Repair Suspension Systems, Frames/Sub Frames and Components
4. 5168.04—Verify Repair of Suspension Systems, Frames/Sub Frames and Components

## SECTION 5169, STEERING SYSTEMS

1. 5159.01—Perform Visual Inspection
2. 5169.02—Diagnose and Troubleshoot Steering Systems and Components
3. 5169.03—Repair Steering Systems and Components

15

4. 5169.04—Verify Repair of Steering Systems and Components
5. 5169.05—Align Steering Axles and Suspension

## SECTION 5170, BRAKING SYSTEMS

1. 5170.01—Perform Visual Inspection
2. 5170.02—Diagnose and Troubleshoot Hydraulic Braking Systems and Components
3. 5170.03—Repair Hydraulic Braking Systems and Components
4. 5170.04—Verify Repair of Hydraulic Braking Systems and Components
5. 5170.05—Diagnose and Troubleshoot Anti-Lock Braking Systems (ABS) and Components
6. 5170.06—Repair Anti-Lock Braking Systems (ABS) and Components
7. 5170.07—Verify Repair of Anti-Lock Braking Systems (ABS) and Components
8. 5170.08—Diagnose and Troubleshoot Anti-Skid/Traction Control Systems and Components
9. 5170.09—Repair Anti-Skid/Traction Control Systems and Components
10. 5170.10—Verify Repair of Anti-Skid/Traction Control Systems and Components
11. 5170.11—Diagnose and Troubleshoot Air Braking Systems and Components
12. 5170.12—Repair Air Braking Systems and Components
13. 5170.13—Verify Repair of Air Braking Systems and Components

## SECTION 5171, TIRES, WHEELS, RIMS AND HUBS

1. 5171.01—Perform Visual Inspection
2. 5171.02—Diagnose and Troubleshoot Tires and Components
3. 5171.03—Repair Tires and Components
4. 5171.04—Verify Repair of Tires and Components
5. 5171.05—Balance Tires and Components

## SECTION 5172, HEATING, VENTILATION AND AIR-CONDITIONING SYSTEMS

1. 5172.01—Perform Visual Inspection
2. 5172.02—Diagnose and Troubleshoot Air-Conditioning Systems and Components
3. 5172.03—Repair Air-Conditioning Systems and Components
4. 5172.04—Verify Repair of Air-Conditioning Systems and Components
5. 5172.05—Diagnose and Troubleshoot Heating and Ventilation Systems and Components
6. 5172.06—Repair Heating and Ventilation Systems and Components
7. 5172.07—Verify Repair of Heating and Ventilation Systems and Components

## SECTION 5173, BODY AND TRIM

1. 5173.01—Perform Visual Inspection
2. 5173.02—Diagnose and Troubleshoot Body and Trim
3. 5173.03—Repair Body and Trim
4. 5173.04—Verify Repair of Body and Trim

## SECTION 5174, EXHAUST, INTAKE AND EMISSION CONTROL SYSTEMS

1. 5174.01—Perform Visual Inspection, Identifying System Types and Applications
2. 5174.02—Diagnose and Troubleshoot Exhaust, Intake and Emission Control Systems and Components
3. 5174.03—Repair Exhaust, Intake and Emission Control Systems and Components
4. 5174.04—Verify Repair of Exhaust and Intake Systems and Components
5. 5174.05—Diagnose and Turbocharger/Supercharger Systems and Components
6. 5174.06—Repair Turbocharger/Supercharger Systems and Components
7. 5174.07—Verify Repair of Troubleshoot Turbocharger/Supercharger Systems and Components
8. 5174.08—Verify Repair of Level I Emission Systems and Components
9. 5174.09—Diagnose and Troubleshoot Level II Emission Control Systems and Components
10. 5174.10—Repair Level II Emission Control Systems and Components
11. 5174.11—Verify Repair of Level II Emission Control Systems and Components

# Practice Test 1   ➤   5

The following practice test has 125 questions. The answer key can be found on p. 81 and the explanations for the answers can be found on p. 85.

## Block A: Occupational Skills

1. What level of eye protection is required when using an oxy-acetylene torch to cut mild steel?

    A. CSA (Canadian Standards Association)-approved safety glasses.
    B. Goggles with a #5 filter.
    C. Goggles with a #10 filter.
    D. Helmet with a #12 filter.

2. A vehicle being raised on a two-post, double swing-arm hydraulic hoist begins to vibrate. Which of the following is the probable cause of the vibration?

    A. The car is too heavy.
    B. Centre of gravity is offset from the posts.
    C. There is an oil leak in the hoist hydraulic circuit.
    D. The swing arm pads are improperly positioned.

3. Which type of fire extinguisher can be used to safely put out Class A-, B-, C-, and D-category fires?

    A. Foam.
    B. Dry chemical.
    C. Carbon dioxide.
    D. Halogenated agent.

4. Where must procedures for cleaning up a spill be outlined on a potentially hazardous product?

    A. The product label.
    B. Manufacturer Web site.
    C. MSDS (Material data safety sheet).
    D. WHMIS guidelines.

5.  What must be completed within 24 hours of a workplace accident that has caused an injury?

    A.  Labour board report.
    B.  Safety committee accident report.
    C.  WSIB report.
    D.  WHMIS report.

6.  Which type of data storage medium is read optically by a shop computer?

    A.  CD-ROM.
    B.  Hard disk drive.
    C.  3.5-inch diskette.
    D.  Microfiche.

7.  Which publication would contain job-time and parts-cost information?

    A.  Service manual.
    B.  Parts manual.
    C.  Estimate guide.
    D.  Owner's manual.

8.  Where must a VIN (vehicle identification number) be displayed?

    A.  On the engine ID plate.
    B.  Top of dashboard, driver's side.
    C.  Top of dashboard, passenger side.
    D.  On the right rear chassis rail.

9.  By how much can an automotive repair bill legally exceed a job estimate in most Canadian jurisdictions?

    A.  Must not exceed the original estimate.
    B.  By 5%.
    C.  By 10%.
    D.  By 50%.

## Block B: Engine Systems

10. When an automobile engine is run without a thermostat, which of the following conditions would be most likely to result?

    A.  Higher HC and CO emissions.
    B.  Higher $NO_x$ emissions.
    C.  Engine overheat.
    D.  Poor acceleration.

11. What shape is a cold, cam-ground piston?

    A. Tapered.
    B. Round.
    C. Slightly oval.
    D. Slightly flared.

12. What happens to a Plastigage™ strip when friction-bearing clearance decreases?

    A. It changes colour.
    B. It becomes wider.
    C. It remains unchanged.
    D. It becomes narrower.

13. When an interference angle is faced to a valve it would be:

    A. 1°.
    B. 2°.
    C. 5°.
    D. 10°.

14. What must be done if the crankshaft end play exceeds specification?

    A. Replace the crankshaft.
    B. Machine the crankshaft thrust faces.
    C. Shim the crankshaft.
    D. Replace the thrust bearing.

15. What is the correct tool(s) for measuring a cylinder head for warpage?

    A. Dial indicator and magnetic base.
    B. Straight edge and feeler gauges.
    C. Outside micrometer.
    D. Dial bore gauge.

16. When a cylinder head valve is equipped with 2 valve springs, what else should be true?

    A. Coil thickness must be identical.
    B. Both must have the same spring rate.
    C. They are wound oppositely.
    D. Valve rotators must be used.

17. What will result if a full-flow oil filter plugs on sediment?

    A. Engine failure.
    B. Filter explodes.
    C. Crankshaft failure.
    D. Bypass valve flows oil around the filter assembly.

18. A V6 engine with a zirconium dioxide-type oxygen sensor has 1 defective spark plug. Which of the following conditions would be most likely to result?

    A. High NO$_x$ emissions.
    B. Underfuelling of all cylinders and cooler engine operation.
    C. Overfuelling of all cylinders and overheating.
    D. Shutdown of companion to dead cylinder.

19. A gasoline-fuelled engine starts to ping as soon as it reaches operating temperature but runs well during the warm-up phase. Which of the following could account for the condition?

    A. Octane rating of the fuel is low.
    B. Octane rating of the fuel is high.
    C. Advanced ignition timing.
    D. Retarded ignition timing.

20. Which of the following conditions would create an increase in fuel rail pressure in a sequential port, gasoline fuel-injection system?

    A. Defective knock sensor.
    B. High altitude operation.
    C. Vacuum drop-off.
    D. Vacuum increase.

21. Which of the following best describes what happens when the armature of a gasoline fuel injector is energized when an engine is running?

    A. Accumulator opens.
    B. Injector closes.
    C. Fuel is injected.
    D. DTC (diagnostic trouble code) is logged.

22. When an engine with sequential port fuel injection is difficult to start after being shut down overnight, but otherwise performs well, which of the following would most likely account for the condition?

    A. Leaking fuel rail.
    B. Defective accumulator or fuel pump check valve.
    C. Inoperative fuel pump relay.
    D. Worn out fuel pump vanes.

23. A standard-type oxygen (lambda) sensor outputs a voltage signal of 0.35 volts DC. Which of the following should be true?

    A. Fuelling is lean.
    B. Fuelling is stoichiometric.
    C. Fuelling is rich.
    D. Oxygen sensor is defective.

24. Which of the following should be done before removing a port-fuel injection injector?

   A. Disconnect the PCM.
   B. Disconnect the fuel pump harness.
   C. Relieve fuel pressure.
   D. Apply vacuum to the fuel pressure regulator.

25. When performing an injector balance test on a sequential injection engine, what would be the most likely cause of an injector that has a lower than normal pressure drop when activated?

   A. Open injector.
   B. Shorted injector.
   C. Plugged injector.
   D. PCM injector-driver fault.

26. When a gasoline fuel injector is grounded when the engine is running, what happens?

   A. Fuelling.
   B. End of fuelling.
   C. DTC is logged.
   D. Injector magnetic field collapses.

27. Which of the following is true of a typical sequential-port gasoline fuel injector?

   A. Actuated by an AC voltage spike.
   B. Ground side controlled by ECM.
   C. Power side controlled by ECM.
   D. Opened by a spring when energized.


## Block C: Vehicle Management Systems

28. How many characters does an OBD II (on-board diagnostics, generation 2) diagnostic code have?

   A. 2.
   B. 3.
   C. 5.
   D. 8.

29. An exhaust manifold is cracked. What type of signal would an oxygen sensor feed to the ECM?

   A. Stoichiometric condition.
   B. Rich fuel condition.
   C. Lean fuel condition.
   D. DTC.

30. Which sensor should indicate a value close to barometric pressure in a naturally aspirated, gasoline-fuelled engine?

    A. MAP sensor.
    B. TP sensor.
    C. ECT sensor.
    D. TBS sensor.

31. When an NTC (negative temperature coefficient) ECT (engine coolant temperature) sensor is subjected to heat, what happens to its internal resistance?

    A. Remains unchanged.
    B. Increases.
    C. Decreases.
    D. Dead shorts.

32. Which of the following actions would remove the data logged into a NV-RAM (non-volatile, random access memory) chip?

    A. Cycling the ignition switch.
    B. Turning the engine off.
    C. Disconnecting the MAF sensor.
    D. Disconnecting the vehicle battery.

33. What is the length of time the ignition module allows current to flow through the coil primary winding known as?

    A. Dwell.
    B. Coil saturation.
    C. Base timing.
    D. Inductive kick.

34. What would remedy a complaint that a spark plug was running hot?

    A. Plug with a longer ceramic insulator.
    B. Plug with a shorter ceramic insulator.
    C. Plug with shorter protrusion into the cylinder head.
    D. Plug with longer protrusion into the cylinder head.

35. When a knock sensor signals a detonation condition, what does the ECM do to rectify the condition?

    A. Inject less fuel.
    B. Inject more fuel.
    C. Retard ignition timing.
    D. Advance ignition timing.

36. When testing an ignition coil with a 3-light logic probe, what is indicated when the yellow light illuminates?

    A. Voltage exceeds 10 V.
    B. Voltage exceeds 4 V.
    C. Voltage is zero.
    D. Voltage is changing.

37. In a typical DIS (distributorless ignition system), described as a waste spark system, which of the following should be true?

   A. 2 spark plugs per cylinder.
   B. 2 ignition coils per cylinder.
   C. 1 coil for every 2 spark plugs.
   D. A single ignition coil is used.

38. What happens when an electronic ignition system "opens" an ignition-switching transistor?

   A. Ignition primary system "opens" and causes the coil to discharge high voltage.
   B. Ignition primary system "closes" and causes the coil to discharge high voltage.
   C. Ignition coil is de-energized.
   D. Magnetic field collapses in the Hall-effect switch.

39. What is the manufacturer-preferred method of removing a thin layer of carbon buildup on an oxygen sensor?

   A. Immerse in carburetor cleaner.
   B. Glass bead blast.
   C. Remove and immerse in an ultra-sonic bath.
   D. Run the engine lean for 2 minutes to heat the sensor.

40. A diesel engine with a rotary distributor injection pump runs well at idle but is sluggish and lacks power under load. Which of the following should be performed first?

   A. Remove the injection pump and send to pump shop.
   B. Check fuel pump static timing.
   C. Check the timing advance circuit.
   D. Remove #1 high-pressure line and spill time.

41. What speed is a rotary diesel fuel injection pump driven at in relation to engine speed on a 4-stroke cycle diesel?

   A. Half engine speed.
   B. Engine speed.
   C. 2 times engine speed.
   D. 4 times engine speed.

42. When a vehicle has a code P0171—System Too Lean (Bank 1), which of the following would be a likely cause?

   A. Restricted fuel return.
   B. Defective oxygen sensor (B1S1).
   C. Brake booster diaphragm rupture.
   D. 1 leaking injector.

43. Which of the following powertrain controller inputs would be useful to monitor to diagnose a transmission shifting problem?

    A. MAP.
    B. MAF.
    C. VSS.
    D. TPS.

44. Which of the following could lead to an intermittent P0605—Internal Control Module ROM (Read-Only Memory) Error?

    A. Shorted 5V reference line to TPS, MAP and MAF sensors.
    B. Cracked internal control module motherboard.
    C. Bent pin on ROM chip.
    D. Low system voltage.

45. Which of the following should be used to properly test PCM wiring?

    A. Multimeter lead.
    B. Paper clip.
    C. Intrusive test clip.
    D. Acupuncture probes.

46. If a PCM had a driver-circuit failure, which of the following would be affected?

    A. IAC.
    B. MAF.
    C. BARO.
    D. Crank sensor.

47. Which of the following is necessary to verify after a repair has been completed on a 2-wire magnetic pulse generator sensor wire?

    A. Voltage drop.
    B. Wire twist.
    C. Harness thickness.
    D. Pin tension.

48. Which of the following should be worn while working on a dash equipped with a disconnected air bag module?

    A. Work boots.
    B. Nylon clothing.
    C. Anti-static strap.
    D. Safety glasses.

49. An OBD II-equipped vehicle has an illuminated anti-lock brake lamp later followed by an illuminated malfunction indicator lamp. Scan data shows a code P0300—Random/Multiple Cylinder Misfire Detected. Which of the following is a likely cause?

    A. Rough roads.
    B. Ignition module.
    C. Inoperative fuel pressure regulator.
    D. Defective camshaft position sensor.

50. Which of the following code types is emission-related and request MIL illumination on the second consecutive trip with a fail condition?

    A. Type A.
    B. Type B.
    C. Type C or (C1).
    D. Type D or (C0).

51. What is the most effective verification of an oxygen sensor fix on an OBD II-equipped vehicle after code clearing?

    A. Perform scan analysis while idling.
    B. Perform scan analysis while driving.
    C. Complete an exhaust gas analysis.
    D. Complete a full OBD II drive cycle.

52. A CAN (Controller Area Network)-equipped vehicle has an excessive parasitic draw. Which of the following could cause this condition?

    A. Defective BCM (body control module).
    B. Keyless entry module.
    C. Anti-theft module.
    D. Blown airbag module fuse.

53. The automatic climate control on a CAN-equipped vehicle is inoperative after a routine service. Which of the following could cause this malfunction?

    A. Loss of refrigerant.
    B. Battery disconnect.
    C. Defective climate control head.
    D. ECM EEPROM failure.

54. After replacing a computer module on an OBD II-equipped vehicle, a flash procedure must be done on the new module. Which of the following is recommended before flashing the new module?

    A. Keep a battery charger on to ensure system voltage.
    B. Always use remote programming.
    C. Check DLC pin tension.
    D. Ensure latest software is downloaded to flash PC.

# Block D: Drive Line Systems

55. How much ATF (automatic transmission fluid) is required to raise the level from add to full when an automatic transmission is at operating temperature?

    A. Half a litre.
    B. 1 litre.
    C. 2 litres.
    D. 4 litres.

56. Which of the following would produce an overdrive in a simple planetary gearset?

    A. Input sun gear, hold ring gear, output carrier.
    B. Input ring gear, hold sun gear, output carrier.
    C. Input carrier, hold ring gear, output sun gear.
    D. Input sun gear, hold carrier, output ring gear.

57. A driver complains that his automatic transmission seems to slip during shifting. The fluid level and condition check out to be normal. Which of the following would be the most likely cause of this condition?

    A. Defective shift logic.
    B. Fluid aeration.
    C. Sticking torque converter stator.
    D. Band adjustment.

58. When pressure-testing a typical automatic transmission on a road test, what would be the maximum acceptable drop-off between shifts?

    A. 5 psi (35 kPa).
    B. 15 psi (100 kPa).
    C. 30 psi (200 kPa).
    D. 60 psi (400 kPa).

59. When an automatic transaxle dipstick is wiped on a clean wiper, there is evidence of dark particles. Which of the following would be the most likely cause?

    A. Wear debris from the transmission metal components.
    B. Severely overheated transmission fluid.
    C. Wear debris from clutches and bands.
    D. Road dust.

60. During a 5-second stall test on an automatic transaxle, the engine rpm rises above the manufacturer's specification. Which of the following is indicated?

    A. Torque-converter stator clutch is slipping.
    B. Engine problem.
    C. Flexplate problem.
    D. Transmission problem.

61. Which is the most accurate method of identifying and correcting a driveshaft vibration on a rear-wheel drive vehicle?

    A.  Trial and error with a hose clamp.
    B.  Knock weight washers off and start from scratch.
    C.  Transducer and strobe light.
    D.  Dial indicator.

62. When an engine is running and the clutch is engaged, what is the friction disc doing?

    A.  Free-wheeling.
    B.  Clamped to the flywheel.
    C.  Free of pressure-plate pressure.
    D.  Rotating at transmission output shaft speed.

63. During a road test, a manual transmission jumps out of gear. Which of the following conditions would be most likely to cause the problem?

    A.  Oil-soaked clutch friction disc.
    B.  Improper clutch adjustment.
    C.  Weak detent springs.
    D.  Worn output shaft bearing.

64. Where is a plunge CV joint located?

    A.  Outboard.
    B.  Inboard.
    C.  In rear-wheel driveshafts.
    D.  Between the engine and transaxle.

65. When a manual clutch is disengaged on a stationary vehicle with the engine running at idle, which of the following should be true?

    A.  The clutch pressure plate is stationary.
    B.  The clutch pilot bearing is stationary.
    C.  The clutch friction disc is stationary.
    D.  The flywheel is stationary.

66. A driver complains that his clutch drags when disengaged. Which of the following could cause this condition?

    A.  Glazed friction faces.
    B.  Loose flywheel bolts.
    C.  Clutch misalignment.
    D.  Warped pressure plate.

67. What is the function of a pilot shaft when installing a new clutch?

    A.  Align the transmission with the flywheel housing.
    B.  Ensure concentricity of the crankshaft with the bell housing.
    C.  Align the friction disc splines with the pilot bearing.
    D.  Ensure concentricity of the pressure plate with the flywheel housing.

68. A differential is noisy on both right and left turns but is otherwise quiet. Which of the following conditions should be checked out first?

    A. Worn differential pinion gears.
    B. Worn drive pinion bearings.
    C. A defective axle bearing.
    D. Worn crown gear bearings.

69. In which of the following applications would a constant velocity joint not be used?

    A. Rear-wheel drive vehicles.
    B. Front-wheel drive vehicles.
    C. Rear-wheel drive with semi-independent rear suspension.
    D. 4-wheel drive with transfer case.

70. What is usually used to set drive pinion depth of mesh into the ring gear in a final drive?

    A. Shims.
    B. Adjusting screw.
    C. Preload torque.
    D. Driveshaft length.

71. When an axle drive shaft imparts drive torque without supporting any of the vehicle weight, how should it be described?

    A. Full-floating.
    B. Three-quarters floating.
    C. Semi-floating.
    D. Solid.

72. When a howling noise is produced by a final drive carrier, what should be done first?

    A. Replace the bearings.
    B. Overhaul the unit.
    C. Check the driveshaft U-joints.
    D. Check the lubricant level.

## Block E: Electrical and Comfort Control Systems

73. Which specific gravity reading taken at 20°C would indicate that a lead acid battery was fully charged?

    A. 1.100.
    B. 1.165.
    C. 1.225.
    D. 1.265.

74. Which of the following tests would be most effective in identifying the location of high resistance in a starting circuit?

    A. Resistance test with an ohmmeter.
    B. Current draw test with an ammeter.
    C. Voltage drop test with a voltmeter.
    D. Check OBD II fault codes.

75. Which of the following should be true when jump-starting a car with a dead battery with another vehicle?

    A. The last connection should be ground on the dead vehicle.
    B. The first connection should be positive on the running vehicle.
    C. The last connection should be positive on the running vehicle.
    D. The first connection should be ground on the dead vehicle.

76. A starter motor will not crank and the vehicle headlamps remain bright. Which of the following could account for the condition?

    A. Corroded battery-positive terminal.
    B. Corroded battery-negative terminal.
    C. Field coils in starter shorted to ground.
    D. Defective neutral safety switch.

77. A starter motor will not crank and the vehicle headlamps dim when the ignition circuit is energized. Which of the following should be checked for first?

    A. Discharged battery.
    B. Corroded terminals.
    C. Field coils in starter shorted to ground.
    D. Armature shorted to ground.

78. When checking starter current draw with an inductive ammeter clamp, which of the following should be done?

    A. Disconnect the battery ground terminal.
    B. Disconnect the alternator.
    C. Crank the engine.
    D. Run the engine at idle speed.

79. What is the maximum voltage drop for any given wire or connection on an alternator?

    A. 0.2 V-DC.
    B. 0.5 V-DC.
    C. 1.0 V-DC.
    D. 1.5 V-DC.

80. What would be the likely result of a poorly grounded voltage regulator?

    A. Discharged battery.
    B. Burned out alternator.
    C. Arcing noise in alternator.
    D. Excessively high charging voltage.

31

81. Which of the following is being done to an alternator when battery voltage is applied directly to the field terminals?

   A. Shorting.
   B. Full-loading.
   C. Full-fielding.
   D. Zero-loading.

82. If an ohmmeter reads infinity between any 2 of the stator winding leads, which of the following would be true?

   A. The stator is properly functional.
   B. The stator windings are shorted.
   C. The stator is open and defective.
   D. The diode bridge is open.

83. When setting up to test the amperage output of an alternator, where should the clamps of a carbon pile tester be located?

   A. Battery positive and battery negative.
   B. Alternator B+ and ground.
   C. Alternator B+ and alternator F terminal.
   D. Starter motor positive and alternator B+.

84. Where should the leads of a DVOM be placed to check for excessive key-off current drain using an ohmmeter on a vehicle battery?

   A. Disconnect battery ground and check between main ground terminal and chassis.
   B. Disconnect battery-positive cable and check between it and the chassis.
   C. Suspected current drain cannot be checked with an ohmmeter.
   D. Disconnect alternator BAT+ and check between it and chassis.

85. Which of the following would more likely be used as a wake-up trigger to a body control module on a vehicle with an electronic dash?

   A. Ignition switch.
   B. Accelerator pedal switch.
   C. Driver side-door switch.
   D. Seat-belt switch.

86. Both headlamps on a vehicle illuminate but are dim. After cleaning the lens, which of the following should be done first?

   A. Replace both headlamp elements.
   B. Replace the dimmer switch.
   C. Replace the headlamp switch.
   D. Check the headlamp ground integrity.

87. Which of the following is true when refrigerant leaves the compressor in an A/C system?

   A. Low-pressure liquid.
   B. Low-pressure gas.
   C. High-pressure liquid.
   D. High-pressure gas.

88. What oil(s) must be used in automotive HFC-134a air-conditioning systems?

   A. PAG only.
   B. Mineral oils only.
   C. Ester only.
   D. PAG and ester in R-12 retrofit systems.

89. In which of the following components is refrigerant boiled to a vapour?

   A. Compressor.
   B. Evaporator.
   C. Dryer.
   D. Condenser.

90. In a three-position A/C stem valve, what is the normal operating position?

   A. Front-seated.
   B. Mid-position.
   C. Back-seated.
   D. Open.

91. When evacuating an HFC-134a A/C system, how long should the vacuum reading be held at 29.9" (76 cm) of Hg (mercury)?

   A. 30 minutes.
   B. 15 minutes.
   C. 10 minutes.
   D. 5 minutes.

92. What type of HFC-134a leak-detection method is the most accurate in detecting the smallest leaks?

   A. Fluorescent leak tracer.
   B. Electronic leak detector.
   C. Flame-type propane leak detector.
   D. Soapy water solution.

93. Which of the following is a likely indication of low refrigerant charge in an HFC-134a A/C system?

   A. Compressor damage.
   B. Higher than normal gauge readings.
   C. Noisy compressor operation.
   D. Faster than normal clutch switch cycling.

94. Which of the following HVAC control doors determines whether ventilation air flows through the heater core?

    A.  Mode door.
    B.  Defroster door.
    C.  Blend door.
    D.  Heater door.

95. Which of the following is the most important personal safety precaution when working around vehicle batteries?

    A.  Wear acid-resistant coveralls.
    B.  Wear CSA-approved leather gauntlets.
    C.  Never touch an energized battery.
    D.  Wear CSA-approved safety glasses.

96. Which of the following substances will do the best job of safely neutralizing battery acid?

    A.  Water.
    B.  Baking soda and water.
    C.  Caustic soda.
    D.  Petroleum solvent.

97. Which of the following is an accurate, dynamic method of testing the operation of electronically controlled, automatic-transmission solenoid valves?

    A.  Using a hand-held lab scope on a road test.
    B.  Checking resistance with an ohmmeter.
    C.  Measuring voltage at the coil.
    D.  Listening for a clicking noise when actuated.

## Block F: Steering, Suspension, Braking, and Cooling Systems

98. When bleeding the brakes on a car with a metering valve using a pressure bleeder, which of the following must be performed?

    A.  The metering valve must be held closed.
    B.  The metering valve should be left alone.
    C.  The metering valve should be held open.
    D.  The proportioning valve should be held closed until the front brakes are bled.

99. What tool should be used to check disc brake rotor runout?

    A.  Straight edge and feeler gauge.
    B.  Outside micrometer.
    C.  Inside micrometer.
    D.  Dial indicator.

100. When measuring TIR (total indicated runout) on a rotor, a positive reading of 1 mm and a negative reading of 1.5 mm is recorded through one rotation. What is the TIR?

   A.   0.5 mm (0.020").
   B.   1.0 mm (0.039").
   C.   1.5 mm (0.059").
   D.   2.5 mm (0.098").

101. What tool is required to measure disc brake rotor parallelism?

   A.   Straight edge and feeler gauge.
   B.   Outside micrometer.
   C.   Inside micrometer.
   D.   Dial indicator.

102. When a brake pedal is applied with steady pressure, the pedal slowly travels to the floor. There is no evidence of external leakage. Which of the following would be the most likely cause of the problem?

   A.   Defective residual check valve.
   B.   Plugged inlet port.
   C.   Leaking master cylinder primary cup.
   D.   Leaking master cylinder secondary cup.

103. Which of the following conditions would be most likely to cause brake fade in a drum brake system?

   A.   A single panic stop.
   B.   Wet brakes.
   C.   Braking in extreme cold.
   D.   Repeated braking during a long downhill gradient.

104. A road test reveals that excessive brake-pedal effort is required to stop a vehicle. Which of the following would be a more likely cause?

   A.   Worn friction facings.
   B.   Air in the hydraulic circuit.
   C.   Water in the hydraulic circuit.
   D.   Power-assist malfunction.

105. Which of the following would be a correct method of depressurizing an ABS system prior to servicing a brake caliper assembly?

   A.   Bleed down engine vacuum.
   B.   Depress brake pedal 40 times with the engine off.
   C.   Depress brake pedal 40 times with the engine on.
   D.   Crack open the master cylinder line nuts.

106. During a road test of a vehicle equipped with disc brakes, the brake pedal pulsates when the brakes are applied. Which of the following could account for this complaint?

    A. Plugged master cylinder compensating port.
    B. Aerated hydraulic fluid.
    C. Moisture-contaminated fluid.
    D. A warped rotor.

107. Which of the following would identify the output of an ABS wheel speed sensor?

    A. Measuring the supply voltage.
    B. Spinning wheel and measuring V-AC.
    C. Spinning wheel and measuring V-DC.
    D. Measuring resistance across the sensor terminals.

108. When machining disc brake rotors, how much material should be removed on the finish cut?

    A. 0.002" (0.051 mm).
    B. 0 008" (0.20 mm).
    C. 0.012" (0.30 mm).
    D. 0.020" (0.50 mm).

109. In a heavy-duty vehicle air brake system using double chamber spring brakes, what force is used to actuate the emergency brakes?

    A. Air pressure.
    B. Spring pressure.
    C. Hydraulic pressure.
    D. Mechanical lever.

110. Which of the following driving conditions will electronic traction control most likely prevent?

    A. Hard acceleration.
    B. Skidding.
    C. Panic braking.
    D. Differential spinout.

111. A front axle tire shows evidence of feathering wear biased toward the outside of the tire. Which of the following is the more likely cause?

    A. Excessive toe-out.
    B. Excessive toe-in.
    C. Improper drag link adjustment.
    D. Steering rack not centered.

112. When a tire is under-inflated, where will the wear be most noticeable?

    A. Sidewall.
    B. Centre of the tire.
    C. Outside edges of the tire.
    D. Inside edges of the tire.

113. What is the maximum pressure an automobile tire can be inflated to when attempting to seat a bead into the rim?

    A.   35 psi (240 kPa).
    B.   50 psi (345 kPa).
    C.   80 psi (552 kPa).
    D.   100 psi (690 kPa).

114. Which type of wheel balance provides the most precision and for this reason would be used on high-performance applications?

    A.   Bench-type static balancer.
    B.   Bench-type dynamic balancer.
    C.   On-the-car spin balancer.
    D.   Off-the car computer balancer.

115. When installing a tire to a rim, which of the following steps will ensure that airflow through the valve is greatest so that the bead is properly seated?

    A.   Lubricating the valve core with rubber lube.
    B.   Removing the valve core during inflation.
    C.   Setting the air compressor regulator to its highest setting.
    D.   Igniting an ether charge within the tire.

116. In a typical rack-and-pinion steering gear, where is the most wear experienced?

    A.   Pinion.
    B.   Centre of rack.
    C.   Extremities of rack.
    D.   Racks are designed to wear evenly.

117. Why should a steering rack preload adjustment not be performed when the rack is known to be worn over high point (centre)?

    A.   Manufacturers advise against performing preload adjustments.
    B.   Most wear takes place on the rack extremities.
    C.   It will result in high point binding.
    D.   It will result in binding on turns.

118. Of the 5 alignment angles, which 3 are normally adjustable on a modern automobile?

    A.   Caster, camber, and toe.
    B.   Turning radius, SAI (steering axis inclination) and toe.
    C.   Toe, turning radius, and camber.
    D.   SAI, toe, and caster.

119. When performing a 4-wheel computer alignment, which of the following should be true?

    A.   Toe is only adjusted on the front wheels.
    B.   Alignment gauges are installed only on the front wheels.
    C.   The steering wheel should be in the straight ahead position.
    D.   Thrust angle is calculated by front-wheel orientation only.

## Block G: Body Components, Trim, and Restraint Systems

120. What activates an SRS (supplemental safety restraint) air bag if the vehicle battery is destroyed on impact?

    A. Engine ECM.
    B. Backup capacitor.
    C. Inertia.
    D. Backup battery.

121. When a passenger's seat belt is unfastened and the ignition circuit is on, what else should be true?

    A. Engine will not start.
    B. SRS air bag circuit will not activate.
    C. Dash warning light is illuminated.
    D. Fault code is logged in engine ECM.

122. When attempting to identify a plastic material, which of the following will give off dense black smoke when ignited?

    A. ABS group plastics.
    B. Polypropylene group plastics.
    C. Vinyl group plastics.
    D. Nylon group plastics.

123. A window washer pumps fluid all of the time the wipers are operated on a vehicle. Which of the following should be checked out first?

    A. Open in switch control circuit.
    B. Blown wiper circuit fuse.
    C. Wiper control switch.
    D. Sticking ratchet wheel on washer pump.

124. What must be done before pulling a steering wheel fitted with an air bag?

    A. Deploy the air bag.
    B. Remove the air bag controller.
    C. Put an anti-static strap around the air bag wiring harness.
    D. Disconnect the air bag wiring harness.

125. After installing trailer-hitch wiring and then testing with the trailer connected, the signal fuse continually blows. Which of the following could be a likely cause?

    A. Open left rear trailer bulb.
    B. Weak flasher unit.
    C. One shorted trailer socket.
    D. Pinched ground wire at trailer tongue.

# Practice Test 2 ➤ 6

The following practice test has 125 questions. The answer key can be found on p. 82 and the explanations for the answers can be found on p. 101.

## Block A: Occupational Skills

1. To prevent asbestos dust from being inhaled, what should you do?

   A. Use compressed air to blow it away.
   B. Use a brush to lightly sweep it away.
   C. Use an aerosol brake cleaner to wash it away.
   D. Use a CSA-approved filter mask.

2. To drill a hole through a steel plate, it is good practice to:

   A. Use a reversible drill.
   B. Use a centre punch to locate the position.
   C. Heat the work to make it softer.
   D. Never hit it with anything hard, because it may shatter.

3. How many requirements are there on an MSDS?

   A. 3.
   B. 5.
   C. 9.
   D. 11.

4. When using an ABC fire extinguisher on a gasoline fire, you must:

   A. Blanket the fire with the extinguisher chemical.
   B. Aim the nozzle at the base of the fire.
   C. Stand at least 6 to 8 metres from the fire.
   D. Pour water on the fire first.

5.  Where should shop solvents and combustible materials be stored?

    A.  Air-tight closets.
    B.  Sealed storage rooms.
    C.  Marked storage cabinets.
    D.  Under workbenches.

6.  A vehicle being raised on an air-over-hydraulic single post, double swing-arm hoist violently jerks when it reaches near full extension. Which of the following could cause this problem?

    A.  Vehicle is too heavy.
    B.  Incorrect pad placements.
    C.  Air in the hydraulic system.
    D.  Broken lift locks.

7.  When is it acceptable to strike a hammer with another hammer?

    A.  Both hammers are of equal weight.
    B.  Never.
    C.  When one hammer is of softer metal.
    D.  When a ball-peen hammer is used.

8.  What should you do if an oxy-acetylene torch starts to emit a loud, high-pitched, squealing noise?

    A.  Run.
    B.  Reduce oxygen pressure.
    C.  Reduce acetylene pressure.
    D.  Shut the torch off.

9.  What angle should a cold chisel be sharpened to?

    A.  45°.
    B.  50°.
    C.  60°.
    D.  65°.

# Block B: Engine Systems

10.  Who is responsible for the vehicle's emission control maintenance?

    A.  Owner.
    B.  Technician.
    C.  Service manager.
    D.  Manufacturer.

11. What should you do with recovered engine coolant (ethylene glycol)?

    A. Pour it down the drain.
    B. Pour it in the waste oil container.
    C. Send it to a recycling operation.
    D. Use it to remove oil stains in the parking lot.

12. What should be done in the event of a significant oil spill in the garage?

    A. Wash the oil down the drain.
    B. Apply oil absorbent, sweep it up, and dispose of it in garbage containers.
    C. Apply oil absorbent, sweep it up, and dispose of it with the waste oil disposal company.
    D. Apply floor soap, scrub, and hose down the drain.

13. Which of the following would be most likely to cause an upper radiator hose collapse on a cold engine?

    A. Defective radiator cap.
    B. Incorrect thermostat rating.
    C. Overheating condition.
    D. Empty overflow tank.

14. What would be the most likely symptom if a turbocharger wastegate was seized in the closed position?

    A. No turbo boost.
    B. High-intake manifold vacuum readings.
    C. Engine knocking.
    D. Low $NO_x$ emissions.

15. Which of the following statements about oil pressure is correct?

    A. It will be high if the bearing clearances are greater than specified.
    B. It will be high if the pressure regulator is seized closed.
    C. It will be low if there are blockages in the oil passages.
    D. It will be low if high-viscosity oil is used in the engine.

16. How should piston-ring groove wear be checked?

    A. Measure the grooves with a machinist's rule and compare to specification.
    B. Install a new piston ring and measure with a feeler gauge between the upper surface of the ring and the land.
    C. Use a depth gauge and check for depth variances around the piston.
    D. Measure and compare the inside and outside diameters of the piston ring.

17. When reinstalling an engine, what would most likely result from an improperly torqued transmission/transaxle bell housing?

    A. Bell housing distortion.
    B. Cracked engine block.
    C. Rearmost engine cylinder pulled out of round.
    D. Crankshaft will crack at rear main.

18. Which of the following problems can be caused by a worn piston pin?

   A. Cold engine knock.
   B. Oil burning (blue smoke emission).
   C. Knocking noise that disappears when cylinder spark plug is grounded out.
   D. Knocking noise that does not disappear when cylinder spark plug is grounded out.

19. A vehicle has an overheating problem in slow, stop-and-go traffic. Which of the following would most likely be the cause?

   A. Stuck open thermostat.
   B. Debris in the radiator fins.
   C. Radiator cap rated at too low pressure.
   D. 70/30 water to antifreeze mixture.

20. When reconditioning an engine block, which machining process should be done first?

   A. Align boring.
   B. Honing the cylinders.
   C. Decking the block.
   D. Cylinder boring.

21. If a fuel pump in an EFI (electronic fuel injection) system primes when the key is initially turned on, but will not start when the engine is cranked, which of the following is the most likely cause?

   A. PCM (powertrain control module) failure.
   B. Fuel pump relay.
   C. Oil pressure switch.
   D. Crankshaft position sensor.

22. Which of the following would cause excessively high fuel pressures?

   A. Broken vacuum line to the regulator.
   B. Clogged fuel injector.
   C. Kinked pressure line.
   D. Restricted return line.

23. A port fuel injection engine has low fuel pressure measured at the fuel rail. Which of the following should be done first?

   A. Replace the fuel filter.
   B. Replace the fuel pump.
   C. Test dynamic pressure downstream from the fuel filter.
   D. Test dynamic pressure downstream from the fuel pump.

24. A throttle-body fuelled engine with dual injectors has good spark but no injector pulse on both injector circuits. Which of the following is the most likely cause?

    A. Defective crank sensor.
    B. Burned fuse.
    C. TPS return signal measuring 0.66 V-DC.
    D. High resistance in the injector ground circuit.

25. When should a port fuel-injected vehicle have the highest fuel pressure?

    A. Closed throttle.
    B. 25% throttle.
    C. 60% throttle.
    D. 100% throttle.

26. On a misfiring gasoline fuel-injected vehicle with adequate spark, the affected cylinder's fuel injector is not audibly working, but has acceptable resistance. Which of the following is the likely cause?

    A. Plugged injector inlet screen.
    B. Shorted injector coil.
    C. Low fuel pressure.
    D. Seized armature.

27. On a no-return circuit type of fuel system, what helps control the fuel pressure when the pressure regulator is located in the fuel tank?

    A. BARO sensor.
    B. Engine vacuum.
    C. MAP sensor.
    D. Oxygen sensor.

## Block C: Vehicle Management Systems

28. Which of the following could contribute to a lean air-fuel mixture in a sequential port, gasoline fuel-injection system?

    A. Restricted air filter.
    B. Leaking lower injector seal.
    C. Leaking upper injector seal.
    D. Broken air duct before the mass airflow sensor.

29. What does a flashing MIL (malfunction indicator lamp) indicate on an OBD II-compliant vehicle?

    A. Misfire that could cause catalytic converter damage.
    B. Type A code.
    C. Type B code.
    D. Internal PCM failure.

30. What does an STFT (short-term fuel trim) value of –10% indicate?

   A. Oxygen sensor is signalling a high voltage condition.
   B. PCM is subtracting fuel to lean out mixture.
   C. PCM is adding fuel to enrich mixture.
   D. System is not in closed loop yet.

31. If an EFI engine has adequate spark and fuel pressure, but still does not start, which of the following is the most likely cause?

   A. TPS signal wire shorted to ground.
   B. TPS signal wire shorted to 5V reference.
   C. Disconnected oxygen sensor.
   D. Fuel pump relay failure.

32. When testing a pulse generator type crankshaft position sensor, what should the output be during cranking?

   A. 500–1500 W.
   B. 1–2 V-DC.
   C. 1–2 V-AC.
   D. 1–2 amps.

33. A VAF (vane airflow meter) is measuring 2.6 V-DC with the engine off. Which of the following should be checked first?

   A. 5V reference signal.
   B. Binding sensor plate.
   C. High resistance in the ground circuit.
   D. Air filter integrity.

34. Which of the following ignition triggering devices produces an alternating current (V-AC) signal?

   A. Hall effect.
   B. Optical.
   C. Magnetic.
   D. Breaker points.

35. What would cause an abnormally low firing line on one cylinder of a DIS?

   A. Fouled spark plug.
   B. Shorted spark plug.
   C. Broken valve spring.
   D. Retarded timing.

36. When a single cylinder is misfiring on a fully warmed engine, what would the oxygen sensor signal to the ECM?

   A. Open loop.
   B. Rich fuel mixture.
   C. Lean fuel mixture.
   D. Closed loop.

37. What happens to ignition timing when engine speed increases?

   A. It advances.
   B. It remains constant.
   C. It retards.
   D. It varies inversely with the engine speed.

38. How many cross-counts should an oxygen sensor produce on a fuel-injected engine operating in closed loop at 2000 rpm?

   A. 20–30.
   B. 28–32.
   C. 1–5.
   D. 1–50.

39. What is the most likely cause of a spark line on an electronic ignition scope pattern having 4 distinct oscillations when the engine is idling?

   A. Too wide spark plug gap.
   B. Shorted ignition coil.
   C. Partially open EGR valve.
   D. Improper crank sensor resistance.

40. A gasoline engine with a knock sensor lacks power and is sluggish under load. Which of the following is the most likely cause?

   A. Mechanical engine knock.
   B. Disconnected knock sensor.
   C. High octane fuel.
   D. Base timing out 2°.

41. A diesel engine runs rough and is smoking excessively. Which of the following would be the most likely cause?

   A. Restricted fuel line.
   B. Leaking injector nozzle.
   C. Restricted exhaust system.
   D. Seized open turbocharger wastegate.

42. The live data output on a scan tool shows a single wire oxygen sensor to be at 0.0 V-DC with the sensor unplugged. Which of the following is the most likely cause?

   A. Oxygen sensor signal wire is open.
   B. Oxygen sensor signal wire is shorted to voltage.
   C. Oxygen sensor signal wire is shorted to ground.
   D. Corrosion between oxygen sensor and exhaust system (poor ground).

43. If an $O_2$ sensor indicates an AFR (rich air fuel ratio), which of the following could cause the condition?

    A. Air leaking into the exhaust manifold.
    B. One or more spark plugs are misfiring.
    C. Low fuel system pressure.
    D. High fuel system pressure.

44. Which of the following OBD II codes would signify trouble in an idle control circuit?

    A. C0505.
    B. P0505.
    C. B0505.
    D. U0505.

45. While manually performing an OBD II drive cycle test, which of the following systems will be tested during 2 1/2 minutes of idling after a start?

    A. EGR.
    B. Catalytic converter.
    C. Canister purge.
    D. Oxygen sensor.

46. An OBD II-equipped vehicle has an illuminated MIL (malfunction indicator light) but will not communicate with the scan tool. What could cause this condition?

    A. Non CAN-compliant scan tool.
    B. Loose DLC pin #11.
    C. Blown PCM fuse.
    D. Low system voltage.

47. Which publication contains procedures for retrieving diagnostic trouble trees?

    A. Service manual.
    B. Parts manual.
    C. Estimation guide.
    D. TSB database.

48. Which of the following on-board controllers should be checked for information on the power windows?

    A. PCM.
    B. VCM.
    C. BCM.
    D. TCM.

49. If a vehicle's on-board diagnostic system publishes a U0029—Vehicle Communication Bus A Performance, which of the following tools should be used to test networking wiring?

    A. Test lamp.
    B. Multimeter.
    C. CAN adapter.
    D. High-speed lab scope.

50. In order to replace a splayed pin on a PCM harness, which of the following should be used?

    A. Pick set.
    B. Terminal tool.
    C. Awl.
    D. Paper clip.

51. OBD II protocol ensures that an MIL will be illuminated when tailpipe emissions exceed Federal Test Procedures by what percentage?

    A. 50%.
    B. 100%.
    C. 150%.
    D. 200%.

52. In order to properly start a drive cycle test to verify a system fix, what should the ECT be less than?

    A. 25°C (77°F).
    B. 50°C (122°F).
    C. 75°C (167°F).
    D. 100°C (212°F).

53. If the active suspension were to incur a fault, what would the generated code start with on an OBD II-compliant vehicle?

    A. P.
    B. S.
    C. U.
    D. C.

54. A V8, OBD II-equipped vehicle harshly hesitates a few minutes after a hot soak restart condition and then runs fine. Which of the following sensors is more likely to cause this condition?

    A. TPS.
    B. VSS.
    C. HO2S.
    D. ECT.

## Block D: Drive Line Systems

55. What is the most likely cause of transmission oil that has a milky appearance?

    A. Overheating.
    B. Water contamination caused by missing dipstick.
    C. Ruptured radiator integral oil cooler.
    D. Engine oil contamination.

56. An electronically controlled automatic transmission is stuck in 3rd gear regardless of gear selector position. What is the most likely cause?

    A. Transmission is in limp-home mode.
    B. Transmission oil has completely leaked out.
    C. Shifter cable fell off.
    D. Air in the valve body.

57. A transmission with a torque converter lock-up solenoid stalls violently when stopping. Which of the following is the most likely cause?

    A. Sticking 2nd-gear servo.
    B. Stuck closed lock-up solenoid.
    C. Engine management problem.
    D. Vehicle speed sensor fault.

58. A rear-wheel drive automatic transmission vehicle has an extremely delayed upshift. Which of the following is the most likely cause?

    A. Restricted oil filter.
    B. Burned clutches.
    C. Defective front pump.
    D. Misadjusted linkages.

59. Which of the following statements is an accurate diagnosis of the results of air-testing a servo?

    A. Hissing sound indicates that the servo is leaking.
    B. There should be no noise coming from the servo or band.
    C. Clunking sound indicates a loose band.
    D. A steady, clicking noise indicates the valve-body check balls are free.

60. Which of the following should be done when inspecting a torque converter?

    A. Check its operation by spinning the turbine in the housing.
    B. Cut the assembly in half to check the condition of the oil pump drive hub.
    C. Make sure the oil pump drive hub and lugs fit loosely in the oil pump.
    D. Check the flex plate to converter bolts and threads.

61. Whenever the carrier in a planetary gear set is the input, the output will always be:

A. Neutral.
B. Reduction.
C. Overdrive.
D. Reverse.

62. Extreme wear is observed on a manual transmission input shaft sleeve. Which of the following should be done to correct the problem?

A. Replace the transmission.
B. Use a repair sleeve and accommodating release bearing.
C. Repair wear marks with weld and refinish with crocus cloth.
D. Install a new release bearing only.

63. Which of the following is most likely caused by low lubricant levels in a manual transmission or transaxle?

A. Gear clashing.
B. Hard shifting.
C. Gear seizure or lockup.
D. Jumping out of gear.

64. When a transaxle is in neutral with the engine running and the clutch engaged, a growling noise is heard. In which of the following is the problem most likely to be?

A. Transaxle input shaft bearings.
B. Intermediate shaft bearings.
C. First/second synchronizer assembly.
D. Pinion and ring gear mesh.

65. Which of the following would be the most likely cause of poor clutch release?

A. Worn clutch fork.
B. Noisy release bearing.
C. Air in the slave cylinder.
D. Worn friction disc.

66. Which of the following is the most common cause of gear clash when it occurs in all gear ratios?

A. Defective synchronizer.
B. Dragging clutch.
C. Slipping clutch.
D. Damaged countershaft gear.

67. After pilot bearing installation, what should it be lubricated with?

A. Plenty of wheel bearing grease.
B. Small amount of lithium grease.
C. Small amount of high-temperature grease.
D. Dielectric compound.

49

68. If backlash is less than specifications in a standard differential, where will the ring gear tooth pattern be?

   A. Close to the heel.
   B. Close to the flank.
   C. Close to the toe.
   D. Close to the face.

69. Which of the following can be done to correct an improper driveline angle on a rear-wheel drive vehicle?

   A. Replace the universal joint.
   B. Wedge rear axle leaf spring.
   C. Change the transmission tailshaft.
   D. Re-torque the pinion nut.

70. A front-wheel drive vehicle makes a clunking noise during a right turn. Which of the following is the most likely cause?

   A. Worn left inboard CV joint.
   B. Worn right inboard CV joint.
   C. Worn left outboard CV joint.
   D. Worn right outboard CV joint.

71. In a rear differential, if the ring gear backlash is improperly adjusted, which of the following would be more likely to occur?

   A. Side bearing overheating.
   B. Pinion bearing wear.
   C. Lubricant leaks.
   D. Rear end whining or clunking.

72. Which of the following components wear extremely rapidly if a vehicle with an open differential is allowed to spin 1 wheel freely for an extended period of time?

   A. Ring gear and pinion.
   B. Side gear teeth.
   C. Pinion bearings.
   D. Pinion and side gear thrust washers.

## Block E: Electrical and Comfort Control Systems

73. After performing a hydrometer test on a fully charged battery, cell 1 has a specific gravity of 1.279 and cell 2 has a specific gravity of 1.225. What should be done to the battery?

   A. Recharge and test.
   B. Return to service.
   C. Replace.
   D. Replace electrolyte.

74. Which of the following would cause a starter motor to whine while engaged?

 A. Defective solenoid.
 B. Worn nose cone roller-bearing set.
 C. Defective flywheel ring gear.
 D. Worn starter brushes.

75. When replacing a starter that can be shimmed, what is the necessary clearance between the flywheel and the starter pinion?

 A. 1/16" (1.59 mm).
 B. 1/8" (3.18 mm).
 C. 3/16" (4.76 mm).
 D. 1/4" (6.35 mm).

76. When cranking an engine, the starter motor turns over slowly. Which of the following is a probable cause?

 A. Neutral safety switch.
 B. Worn starter bushings.
 C. Low resistance in the negative cable.
 D. Excessive battery CCA.

77. A starter motor will not crank and the headlamps dim when the starting circuit is energized. The battery test is acceptable and the connections are corrosion-free. Which of the following should be checked next?

 A. Positive battery cable for an open circuit.
 B. Neutral safety switch for high resistance.
 C. Ignition switch for high resistance.
 D. Starter mounting for flange corrosion.

78. Which of the following is an acceptable maximum AC voltage leakage output from an alternator in a normal load condition?

 A. 0.5–1.0 V-AC.
 B. 0.1–0.5 V-AC.
 C. 1.0–1.5 V-AC.
 D. 13.5–15.5 V-AC.

79. Which of the following could cause excessive alternator whine?

 A. No load operation.
 B. Defective diodes.
 C. Defective rear bearing.
 D. Glazed belt.

80. What is the purpose of using a carbon pile in a charging system diagnostic routine?

 A. Test the battery specific gravity.
 B. Load the battery to initiate alternator to maximum output.
 C. Bypass the PCM control.
 D. Test wiring for opens and shorts.

81. If an ohmmeter reads 1 ohm between the rotor slip rings and the rotor shaft, what is indicated?

   A. Reading is within specification.
   B. Rotor coil windings are open.
   C. Rotor coil windings are shorted to ground.
   D. Rotor coil windings are shorted to each other.

82. A vehicle equipped with a remote starter will start with the key, but not with the remote device. Which of the following is a likely cause?

   A. Defective ignition switch.
   B. Burned ignition fusible link.
   C. Inoperative starter solenoid.
   D. Hood pin switch shorted to ground.

83. A vehicle equipped with a road-speed sensitive, volume-controlled radio does not increase the volume as the road speed increases. Which of the following could be a likely cause?

   A. Defective vehicle speed sensor.
   B. Defective right front-wheel speed sensor.
   C. Open circuit between the vehicle speed sensor and the PCM.
   D. Open circuit between the PCM and the radio.

84. When replacing a non-deployed air bag module, what should be done first?

   A. Disconnect the diagnostic energy reserve module.
   B. Disconnect the battery.
   C. Disconnect the BCM.
   D. Remove the trim screws.

85. After installing an alternator, a high-pitched whine that changes proportionally with engine speed is present with the radio on. Which of the following could correct this problem?

   A. Replace the new alternator because it is probably defective.
   B. Check wiring connections at the radio.
   C. Install an auxiliary ground strap for the alternator.
   D. Install a capacitor to a ground at the alternator output.

86. When testing a dome lamp circuit, 12 V can be measured on both sides of the lamp. What does this indicate?

   A. Defective (open) bulb.
   B. Defective (shorted) bulb.
   C. Short to ground before the switch.
   D. Open ground circuit.

87. What instrument is commonly used to check the coil of an A/C compressor clutch?

   A. Voltmeter.
   B. Ohmmeter.
   C. Ammeter.
   D. Test lamp.

88. In an A/C system, where does refrigerant change from a high-pressure vapour to a high-pressure liquid?

   A. Orifice tube.
   B. Accumulator.
   C. Condenser.
   D. Evaporator.

89. When retrofitting an HFC-134a system in place of an R-12 A/C system, what must be changed?

   A. Receiver-dryer.
   B. Evaporator.
   C. Compressor.
   D. Service fittings.

90. A sight glass used on an HFC-134a system can be used to determine which of the following system problems?

   A. An overcharge condition.
   B. A complete loss of refrigerant.
   C. Low system oil level.
   D. An undercharged condition.

91. A vacuum-operated heater system, regardless of the control position, blows air out the floor vents at all times. Which of the following is the most likely cause?

   A. Inoperative blend door.
   B. Vacuum leak to the control head.
   C. Binding heater door.
   D. Binding motor door.

92. A partially plugged A/C orifice tube will cause which of the following conditions?

   A. Excessively low low-side pressure.
   B. Excessively high low-side pressure.
   C. Rapid cycling of the low-side pressure.
   D. Compressor failure.

93. What controls the flow of refrigerant into the evaporator in an orifice tube system?

   A. A thermostatic sensing device that controls the orifice size.
   B. A throttling valve that controls the evaporator outflow.
   C. A throttling valve that controls the evaporator inflow.
   D. A pressure sensitive switch that turns the compressor clutch on and off.

94. Clear water is found in the passenger compartment of an air-conditioned vehicle. Which of the following is a likely cause?

    A. Leaking heater core.
    B. Plugged heater box drain.
    C. Iced-up evaporator.
    D. Leaking TXV (thermostatic expansion valve).

95. While checking an ABS diagnostic code, the left front wheel is identified as the source of the problem. During testing, AC voltage from the sensor is abnormally low. Which of the following could be the cause?

    A. Shorted 5V reference signal wire.
    B. Improper sensor air gap.
    C. Defective EBCM (electronic brake control module).
    D. Open in sensor wires.

96. If two 120W fog lamps are to be installed on a vehicle, assuming working voltage of 15 V, what size of fuse should be used to properly protect the system?

    A. 10 amps.
    B. 15 amps.
    C. 20 amps.
    D. 25 amps.

97. When installing an amplifier/subwoofer system in a vehicle with a 4-gauge power cable running from the battery positive terminal to the trunk, where is the ideal place for the fuse?

    A. 12" (30 cm) from the positive battery post.
    B. At the firewall.
    C. In the trunk, before the amplifier.
    D. On the ground side.

## Block F: Steering, Suspension, Braking, and Control Systems

98. Which of the following could illuminate the red brake-warning lamp?

    A. Power assist malfunction.
    B. Maladjusted rear drum brakes.
    C. Worn brake shoes.
    D. Broken parking brake pedal return spring.

99. No fluid is seen squirting from the primary compensating port in the master cylinder reservoir on brake application. Which of the following would be the most likely cause?

    A. Brake pedal pushrod adjustment.
    B. Defective secondary cup seal.
    C. Air in the hydraulic circuit.
    D. Defective master cylinder cap seal.

100. A rear-wheel-drive sport utility vehicle has a rear brake lock-up condition when the vehicle is lightly loaded. Which of the following would be the most likely cause of this problem?

    A.  Defective pressure differential switch.
    B.  Defective metering valve.
    C.  Seized proportioning valve.
    D.  Air in the hydraulic circuit.

101. The right front wheel on a diagonally split brake system is excessively hot after a short drive. Which of the following would be the most likely cause?

    A.  Warped rotor.
    B.  Collapsed flex line.
    C.  Defective proportioning valve.
    D.  Seized left rear-wheel cylinder.

102. Which of the following best describes the thrust angle of a vehicle?

    A.  Angle relative to the centreline as determined by the total toe of the front wheels.
    B.  Angle relative to the centreline as determined by the total toe of the front and rear wheels.
    C.  Angle relative to the centreline as determined by the total toe of the rear wheels.
    D.  Angle relative to the centreline as determined by a line drawn perpendicular to the front axle.

103. While inspecting a duo-servo drum brake assembly, the brake shoes do not rest on the anchor. Which of the following could cause the problem?

    A.  Over-adjusted star wheel.
    B.  Weak return springs.
    C.  Seized parking-brake cables.
    D.  Worn brake shoes.

104. Why is a scratch cut performed before rotor machining?

    A.  To ensure the lathe is operating properly.
    B.  To remove any light rust from the rotor.
    C.  To test the brake lathe bits for sharpness.
    D.  To make sure the rotor is centred on the arbor.

105. What must be done to a floating rotor in order to properly measure runout?

    A.  Adjust the wheel bearings.
    B.  Torque wheel nuts on rotor.
    C.  Remove the rotor from the vehicle.
    D.  Open the bleeder screw.

106. During a dynamometer test, the anti-lock brake lamp on a 4-wheel anti-lock, 2-wheel-drive vehicle illuminates. Which of the following could account for this?

    A. Wheel speed sensor problem.
    B. The non-driven wheels are not turning.
    C. ABS was not deactivated.
    D. The dynamometer is producing electro-magnetic interference.

107. A vehicle has excessive runout on the right front, floating-type rotor. While on the lathe, the runout is measured to be within specification. Which of the following could be the problem?

    A. Debris on the mounting flange.
    B. Defective rotor.
    C. Binding CV joint.
    D. Bent knuckle.

108. Which of the following would be the most likely cause of a low brake pedal?

    A. Aerated brake fluid.
    B. Seized wheel cylinder.
    C. Seized front caliper slider pins.
    D. Worn brake pads.

109. Under which of the following conditions would traction control be disabled?

    A. Low brake fluid.
    B. Worn brake pads.
    C. ABS malfunction.
    D. Vacuum-assist malfunction.

110. An air dryer in an air-brake system must be serviced regularly to make sure it can:

    A. Cool air as it enters the brake system.
    B. Provide clean, dry air to the brake system.
    C. Meter desiccant into the brake system.
    D. Match inside air quality to that of outside air.

111. When a tire is over-inflated, where will the wear be most evident?

    A. Sidewall.
    B. Outside edges of the tire.
    C. Centre of the tire.
    D. Bead area.

112. When checking a ball joint with a wear indicator, what would indicate that the ball joint needs to be replaced?

    A. When the shoulder on the wear indicator is exposed.
    B. When the shoulder on the wear indicator is flush with the body.
    C. When the shoulder on the wear indicator is recessed.
    D. When the grease fitting recesses into the joint.

113. Which of the following would most likely account for a clunk or snap from the front-end while turning?

    A. Worn wheel bearings.
    B. Seized strut bearing.
    C. Loose power steering belt.
    D. Bald tires.

114. Which of the following components is usually adjusted to correct parallelism in a parallelogram steering setup?

    A. Idler arm.
    B. Pitman arm.
    C. Centre link.
    D. Power piston.

115. When performing a radial runout test on a tire, where should the dial indicator be placed for the most accurate results?

    A. On the sidewall.
    B. On the rim lip.
    C. On the tire tread.
    D. On the rim lip and the tire tread.

116. A dry park test must be conducted with the vehicle in which of the following conditions?

    A. On level ground.
    B. On radius plates that allow front-wheel movement.
    C. With the wheels suspended (on hoist or vehicle stands).
    D. With the engine running in neutral.

117. Which of the following would be the most likely cause of aerated power steering fluid?

    A. Restricted pump inlet.
    B. Restricted pump outlet.
    C. Fluid leaks.
    D. Slipping drive belt.

118. Which of the following could cause a steering complaint of wandering?

    A. Binding strut bearings.
    B. Torque steer.
    C. Improper steering gear preload.
    D. Brake system imbalance.

119. Which of the following alignment angles is statically measured?

    A. Front camber.
    B. Front caster.
    C. Front toe.
    D. Rear toe.

## Block G: Body Components, Trim, and Restraint Systems

120. How many closed sensors are necessary for air bag deployment?

    A. 1 forward and 1 safing.
    B. 2 forward and 1 safing.
    C. 2 forward only.
    D. 1 safing only.

121. When replacing sensors on a vehicle that has deployed an air bag, it is important to:

    A. Test each sensor with a voltmeter.
    B. Torque all mounting bolts.
    C. Test each sensor with a self-powered test lamp.
    D. Ensure that the sating sensor is armed.

122. The window on the passenger front door does not move up and down, but the motor is audibly working. Which of the following is the most likely cause?

    A. Binding window regulator.
    B. Broken window track.
    C. Window motor switch.
    D. Window is binding in the channels.

123. What normally causes wind noise or whistling around the top of the windscreen?

    A. Door seals leaking due to the door being out of adjustment.
    B. Windscreen trim molding loose or not fully seated to the windscreen.
    C. Roof ditch hem seals do not extend fully forward to the windscreen.
    D. Bent metal window flange.

124. After installing a remote starting device, the vehicle will intermittently shut off only while in remote start mode. Which of the following is a likely cause?

    A. Magnetic interference.
    B. Defective hood pin switch.
    C. Tripping circuit breaker.
    D. Defective remote start module.

125. A vehicle with a factory-equipped theft-deterrent system will start and then shut off 2 seconds later. Which of the following is more likely to be defective?

    A. Transmitter.
    B. Receiver module.
    C. Body controller.
    D. Ignition key.

The following practice test has 125 questions. The answer key can be found on p. 83 and the explanations for the answers can be found on p. 115.

## Block A: Occupational Skills

1. Which class of fire extinguisher would be used if the item on fire was a 120V electrical outlet?

    A.  A.
    B.  B.
    C.  C.
    D.  D.

2. Who has the responsibility for ensuring that workers are wearing proper protective equipment?

    A.  Workers.
    B.  Supervisors.
    C.  Employers.
    D.  OHSC (Occupational Health and Safety Committee).

3. After measuring a hole with a small-bore gauge, what tool would you use to obtain the most accurate measurement?

    A.  Ruler.
    B.  Vernier caliper.
    C.  Inside micrometer.
    D.  Outside micrometer.

4. According to WHMIS regulations, what identifier must a supplier label have?

    A.  Address of workplace.
    B.  Hatched border.
    C.  MSDS information.
    D.  Toxicological information.

5. What do green tire valve caps indicate?

   A. Tire is inflated with hydrogen.
   B. Tire is inflated with nitrogen.
   C. Tire is inflated with regular air.
   D. Nothing, they are simply colour-matched to the vehicle.

6. Since 1981, what position in the VIN (vehicle identification number) indicates the country of origin?

   A. 1st.
   B. 2nd.
   C. 3rd.
   D. 10th.

7. In which of the following service publications would you find information on persistent problems with a vehicle?

   A. Wiring schematics.
   B. Labour guide.
   C. TSBs.
   D. Owner's manual.

8. At what pressure does released acetylene become unstable and possibly explode?

   A. 5 psi (35 kPa).
   B. 15 psi (103 kPa).
   C. 250 psi (1724 kPa).
   D. 3600 psi (24.8 MPa).

9. How often should you check the safety mechanisms on an automotive lifting device?

   A. Daily.
   B. Weekly.
   C. Monthly.
   D. Annually.

## Block B: Engine Systems

10. If the vacuum valve portion of a 15 psi (103.4 kPa) radiator cap is stuck open, which of the following is most likely to happen?

    A. Leakage at the radiator tanks.
    B. No coolant in the overflow reservoir.
    C. Reduced system pressure.
    D. Collapsed upper radiator hose when the engine is cold.

11. If the main spring of a thermostat becomes weak or broken, which of the following is most likely to occur?

  A. Engine will produce more torque.
  B. Engine efficiency will increase.
  C. Pre-ignition will occur.
  D. Hydrocarbon emissions will be elevated.

12. Measured oil pressure is below specifications. Which of the following would be a likely cause?

  A. Weak oil-pressure relief spring.
  B. Stuck closed pressure relief valve.
  C. One partially clogged camshaft gallery.
  D. Oil pump case clearance out of specification by 0.002" (0.051 mm).

13. If compression values increase after performing a "wet" compression test on a cylinder, which engine component should be investigated for damage or failure?

  A. Intake valve.
  B. Exhaust valve.
  C. Compression rings.
  D. Oil-control rings.

14. Which of the following tools is most accurate for checking coolant strength?

  A. Hydrometer.
  B. pH test strips.
  C. Refractometer.
  D. Gas analyzer.

15. If a horizontally mounted thermostat has a "jiggle valve," at what position should the valve be placed?

  A. The bottom.
  B. The top.
  C. The side.
  D. Closest to the heater core.

16. When installing a new gear-type oil pump, which of the following should be done?

  A. Coat the surfaces with used engine oil.
  B. Apply silicone to the tips of the gear teeth.
  C. Leave the oil pump dry; oil from the sump will lubricate.
  D. Coat the pump with assembly lube.

17. Plastigage™ would be used to measure which of the following clearances?

  A. Valve guide clearance.
  B. Camshaft bearing clearance.
  C. Oil pump side clearance.
  D. Swept volume.

18. Which of the following would be the most likely cause of excessive fuel pressure?

   A. Restriction in the fuel supply line.
   B. Excessive current supplied to the fuel pump.
   C. Low engine vacuum.
   D. Restriction in the fuel return line.

19. A vehicle has a single cylinder misfire on a group-type injection system. Which of the following is the more likely cause?

   A. Open injector PCM control circuit.
   B. Blown injector fuse.
   C. Inoperative (open) injector.
   D. Stuck fuel-pressure regulator.

20. What would be the most likely cause of a loud clunking noise when accelerating in forward gear ranges only?

   A. Broken engine mount.
   B. Defective front universal joint.
   C. Loose exhaust manifold.
   D. Broken flex plate.

21. Where should exhaust back pressure be tested in order to find a partially plugged catalytic converter?

   A. At the exhaust manifold gasket.
   B. At the catalytic converter front gasket.
   C. Pre-catalytic oxygen sensor.
   D. Post-catalytic oxygen sensor.

22. Which of the following would be a likely cause of severe piston damage?

   A. Retarded timing.
   B. Detonation.
   C. Open ignition wire.
   D. Over-rich mixture.

23. If measured piston ring side clearance is too great, which of the following might occur?

   A. Binding during installation.
   B. Inadequate oil drainage.
   C. Piston wear.
   D. Ring flutter.

24. If an air injection pump has seized, which of the following is the most likely cause?

   A. Inadequate oil level.
   B. Belt tension too low.
   C. Defective check valve.
   D. Partially open EGR valve.

25. During a cylinder leakage test, air is heard escaping through the oil fill. Which of the following is the correct item to investigate?

   A. Piston rings.
   B. Intake valve.
   C. Exhaust valve.
   D. Head gasket.

26. While honing a cylinder, which of the following should be used?

   A. A boring bar.
   B. Torque plates.
   C. Detergent and water.
   D. A deck grinder.

27. Which of the following is the most likely cause of cylinder block cracking?

   A. Coolant with high pH level.
   B. Collision.
   C. Engine overheating condition.
   D. Metallurgical fatigue.

## Block C: Vehicle Management Systems

28. Which of the following conditions would be the likely cause of a "hard to start" complaint that only occurs when the engine is at operating temperature?

   A. Retarded ignition timing.
   B. Advanced ignition timing.
   C. Shorted crankshaft position sensor.
   D. Fuel contamination of engine oil.

29. A standard oxygen sensor is producing an average reading of 450 mV on an engine that is at operating temperature and assumed to be in closed loop mode. What should happen to the voltage reading if you create a vacuum leak by disconnecting a small vacuum hose?

   A. Nothing.
   B. Voltage reading goes up.
   C. Voltage reading goes down.
   D. Engine stalls.

30. Which of the following input sensors should produce nearly identical readings on a vehicle at the moment of start-up after being shut down for 12 hours?

   A. MAF and MAP.
   B. ECT and IAT.
   C. DTC and TPS.
   D. VSS and CKP.

31. How many pins are in an OBD II-compliant data link connector?

    A. 2.
    B. 8.
    C. 16.
    D. 32.

32. What is the minimum number of data freeze-frames captured by an OBD II-compliant vehicle after a DTC is set?

    A. No minimum.
    B. 1.
    C. 2.
    D. 8.

33. Which vehicle system do all OBD-II Type A and B diagnostic trouble codes relate to?

    A. Engine.
    B. Exhaust.
    C. Emissions.
    D. Climate control.

34. Which pin in a standard 16-pin, OBD II-compliant data link connector is reserved for chassis ground?

    A. 2.
    B. 4.
    C. 8.
    D. 16.

35. How is a *warm-up cycle* defined for purposes of OBD II code log clearance?

    A. 3 consecutive key-on/key-off cycles.
    B. Coolant temperature increase of at least 22°C (71.6°F).
    C. Coolant temperature exceeds 70°C (158°F).
    D. Coolant temperature exceeds 70°C after an increase of at least 22°C.

36. If you unplug a coolant temperature sensor terminal from the coolant sensor on a warm engine, which of the following would result?

    A. The engine will automatically shut down.
    B. Coolant temperature is displayed on scan tool at the highest possible reading.
    C. A DTC is set indicating an open.
    D. A DTC is set indicating voltage high.

37. Which of the following conditions would be more likely to account for a low output voltage from a standard $O_2$ sensor located upstream from the catalytic converter?

  A. Plugged catalytic converter.
  B. Restricted exhaust system.
  C. Failed air injection circuit.
  D. Cracked exhaust manifold.

38. Which of the following running conditions would be more likely to require a richer than stoichiometric air-fuel mixture?

  A. Normal cruising.
  B. Light load operation.
  C. Deceleration.
  D. Idling.

39. An engine fuelled with 89 octane gasoline pings especially when accelerated. The fuel is specified as a 10% ethanol cut. Which of the following would be more likely to remedy the condition?

  A. Advance the base ignition timing.
  B. Change to a higher octane-rated fuel.
  C. Change to a lower octane-rated fuel.
  D. Change to an ethanol-free gasoline.

40. What should result when the vacuum hose on the fuel regulator on a port-injected fuel injection system is removed?

  A. Fuel rail pressure decreases.
  B. Fuel rail pressure increases.
  C. Fuel rail pressure unaffected.
  D. Engine stalls.

41. While performing a noid light test to diagnose a fuel injector problem, the noid light illuminates but appears to be dim. What condition is indicated?

  A. High resistance in the fuel injector coil.
  B. Short circuit in fuel injector harness.
  C. Short circuit in fuel injector coil.
  D. High resistance in the fuel injector wiring or connector.

42. A gasoline fuel pump produces a whine from the fuel tank when it operates. Which of the following should be performed before making the decision to replace the pump?

  A. Replace the fuel filter.
  B. Replace the fuel regulator.
  C. Replace the fuel tank.
  D. Replace the fuel injectors.

43. You have electrically tested a set of injectors on a V6 engine with around 200,000 km on the odometer and found 3 to be defective to the point of requiring replacement. Which of the following would be the correct procedure?

   A.  Keep testing the 3 good injectors to see if you can make them fail.
   B.  Replace the solenoids on the 3 defective injectors.
   C.  Recommend that a set of 6 new injectors be installed.
   D.  Switch the location of the 3 good and 3 defective injectors.

44. When a vacuum hose is removed from a vacuum-modulated fuel pressure regulator, a small quantity of fuel drips from the hose. Which of the following is the more likely cause?

   A.  Excessively high rail pressure.
   B.  Leak in the fuel rail return circuit.
   C.  Leak in the regulator diaphragm.
   D.  Restriction in fuel rail inlet.

45. When scoping a pulse width-actuated injector, where should the inductive kick (spike) occur on the graphic?

   A.  At the end of the pulse width profile.
   B.  At the centre of the pulse width profile.
   C.  At the beginning of the pulse width profile.
   D.  Profile should be entirely "square" if the injector is good.

46. You are scoping one of a set of injectors in a port-injected fuel system and observe the inductive kick displayed in the graphic to gradually reduce in length as the engine warms to operating temperature. What is the likely cause?

   A.  Short in the injector coil.
   B.  Open in the injector coil.
   C.  High resistance in the injector coil.
   D.  Injector pulse width is shortened as the engine reaches operating temperature.

47. If the oxidizing stage of a catalytic converter on a gasoline engine is functioning properly, which of the following should be true regarding exhaust gas temperatures once the engine is at operating temperature?

   A.  Converter in should be 15% warmer than converter-out temperature.
   B.  Converter in and out temperatures should be equal.
   C.  Converter out should be 15% warmer than converter-in temperature.
   D.  Converter should be cool enough to touch by hand.

48. Which type of ignition system eliminates spark plug wires?

   A.  COP (coil on plug).
   B.  DIS.
   C.  Direct fire system.
   D.  Contact point systems.

49. Which of the following must be true of the shield used on an optical ignition sensor?

    A. It must be airtight.
    B. It must be periodically replaced.
    C. It must be lightproof.
    D. It must be lubricated with engine oil prior to installation.

50. When troubleshooting a distributorless ignition system you identify a defective high-tension wire. Which of the following should be replaced along with the wire?

    A. Spark plug.
    B. Coil.
    C. Ballast resistor.
    D. Distributor pick-up coil.

51. What switches primary circuit current in the ignition module in a typical electronic ignition circuit?

    A. Transistor.
    B. Hall-effect switch.
    C. Optical switch.
    D. Electro-mechanical switch.

52. When platinum spark plugs are to be reused, which of the following is correct procedure?

    A. Regap to specification.
    B. Coat threads lightly with anti-seize compound and do not attempt to regap.
    C. Apply 10% more than original specified torque.
    D. Glass bead blast the electrodes.

53. When scoping a good pair of plugs on a waste spark ignition system, what should distinguish the power spark from the waste spark on the oscilloscope pattern?

    A. Firing line is higher on the power plug.
    B. Firing line is lower on the power plug.
    C. Intermediate oscillations diminish more rapidly on waste plug.
    D. Both patterns should be nearly identical through the cycle.

54. When you disconnect a high-tension wire on a running engine while troubleshooting an ignition problem, what must you do?

    A. Prevent the high-tension wire from contacting ground.
    B. Disconnect the ignition module.
    C. Ground the spark plug with a jumper wire.
    D. Ground the high-tension wire.

## Block D: Drive Line Systems

55. Which of the following procedures is most correct to check for a defective universal joint?

    A. Grasp both halves and check for more than 1/8" (3.18 mm) play.
    B. Remove the driveshaft and check for roughness.
    C. Inject grease and see if symptom goes away.
    D. Ensure the boot is not split.

56. Which of the following would most likely cause driveline shudder upon hard acceleration?

    A. Defective front universal joint.
    B. Dry rear universal joint.
    C. Weak leaf springs.
    D. Unbalanced driveshaft.

57. Which of the following would cause noise from a manual transmission only when the clutch is disengaged?

    A. Defective pilot bearing.
    B. Incorrect lubrication.
    C. Dry input shaft bearing.
    D. Weak clutch release fingers.

58. Which of the following could cause slipping in an automatic transmission?

    A. Filter O-ring failure.
    B. High-throttle pressure.
    C. Incorrect throttle kickdown adjustment.
    D. High main line pressure.

59. Which of the following should be used to bench test an automatic transmission clutch pack or servo piston?

    A. Fluid pump.
    B. Air nozzle.
    C. C-clamp.
    D. Dial gauge.

60. Which of the following is likely to occur if the torque converter stator binds and hangs up?

    A. Poor acceleration from start.
    B. Engine stall at a vehicle stop.
    C. Transmission fluid over-cooling.
    D. Lack of power at highway speed.

61. Excessive clutch pedal free play will lead to which of the following conditions?

   A. Harsh shifting.
   B. Clutch slippage.
   C. Premature release bearing failure.
   D. High clutch pedal engagement point.

62. Which of the following could cause a gear-to-gear transfer case to stay in 4-wheel-drive mode?

   A. Sun gear failure.
   B. Worn splines on the transmission output shaft.
   C. Binding shift collar.
   D. Worn front output shaft teeth.

63. If the backlash in a differential is too great, where will ring gear tooth wear patterns show?

   A. Heel.
   B. Toe.
   C. Crest.
   D. Face.

64. What should be done after changing a worn transmission mount?

   A. Check transmission fluid level.
   B. Road test vehicle.
   C. Measure driveline angles.
   D. Re-lubricate slip yoke.

65. Which of the following could cause harsh, crunchy shifts into every gear in a manual gearbox?

   A. All synchronizers' blocking rings are defective.
   B. Bent shift shafts.
   C. Broken tooth on reverse idler.
   D. Incorrect lubricant.

66. Which of the following could cause an electronic automatic transmission to shift hard when hot?

   A. Incorrect lubricant.
   B. Defective 1-2 shift solenoid.
   C. Defective pressure control solenoid.
   D. Plugged filter.

67. Which of the following could prevent an automatic transmission from shifting into manual-low?

   A. Low main line pressure.
   B. Fluid aeration.
   C. Collapsed linkage bushing.
   D. Binding 1-2 shift valve.

68. If a vehicle with an electronically controlled automatic transmission will not shift out of 1st gear, which of the following is a likely cause?

    A. TPS.
    B. Torque converter.
    C. PCS.
    D. TFTS.

69. Which of the following could cause a very harsh clutch application?

    A. Scored flywheel surface.
    B. Worn clutch friction disk.
    C. Weak and broken torsion springs.
    D. Heat spots on the pressure plate.

70. An electronic transmission will not shift into 4th gear (overdrive) but the command from the PCM is given to shift. There are no transmission diagnostic codes. Which of the following is a likely cause?

    A. High main line pressure.
    B. Plugged oil filter.
    C. Misadjusted shift cable.
    D. Worn 4th-gear shaft.

71. When servicing the wheel bearings on a vehicle with locking hubs, which of the following should be done?

    A. Clean and lightly coat the hub components with grease.
    B. Install a new hub cotter pin.
    C. Install the hubs in the engaged position only.
    D. Install all new snap rings.

72. Which of the following is the most likely cause for an output shaft seal leak?

    A. Transmission fluid level high.
    B. Slip yoke worn.
    C. A worn tail shaft bushing.
    D. Worn rear universal joint.

## Block E: Electrical and Comfort Control Systems

73. Which of the following should be used to perform an IOD (ignition-off draw) test on a vehicle?

    A. Ohmmeter.
    B. Ammeter.
    C. Voltmeter.
    D. Jumper wire.

74. You are performing an IOD test on an automobile equipped with multiple computer systems. The engine has been key-off for a 30-minute period and the ammeter reading is 0.045 amps. What should you do next?

    A. Remove all the fuses and retest.
    B. One by one, remove and replace each fuse and retest.
    C. Nothing, 0.045 amps battery drain is acceptable.
    D. Replace the battery.

75. When the conduit on a 12 V-DC insulated electrical wire wears through and it contacts the vehicle frame, what results is known as:

    A. An open.
    B. A fire.
    C. A short to ground.
    D. A short to voltage.

76. If an electrical accessory was spliced into part of the insulated circuit, which of the following would result in the circuit?

    A. Current increase.
    B. Current decrease.
    C. Resistance increases.
    D. Voltage decreases.

77. Which of the following is the preferred method of testing the integrity of a series of standard blade-type fuses in an electrical fuse panel?

    A. Pull each fuse, use DVOM ohmmeter to test continuity.
    B. Pull each fuse, use jumper wires and an ammeter in series.
    C. Use DVOM in V-DC mode and test each fuse in position at shoulder test points.
    D. Pull each fuse and observe fusible medium through the plastic.

78. Which of the following electrical cable sizes would be an appropriate specification for an automobile battery cable?

    A. AWG #2.
    B. AWG #6.
    C. AWG #10.
    D. AWG #14.

79. What colour is used for the high-voltage wiring insulation in high-potential hybrid vehicle electrical circuits?

    A. Red.
    B. Orange.
    C. White.
    D. Blue.

80. The electric horn on a vehicle does not sound. Where should you begin to troubleshoot the malfunction?

    A. At the horn.
    B. At horn circuit fuse.
    C. At the horn button/switch.
    D. At the horn relay.

81. When a battery has to be disconnected from a vehicle, which of the following is the appropriate method for ensuring that no memory loss occurs in any of the vehicle computers networked to the data bus?

    A. Quickly install a backup battery after disconnecting the original.
    B. Install a 9V-DC battery anywhere in the circuit.
    C. Plug a 12V-DC memory saver into a power outlet/lighter socket.
    D. Use booster cables from another vehicle to maintain chassis voltage.

82. The high-voltage battery pack has become discharged on a hybrid-drive vehicle. What should be done to crank and start the engine?

    A. The vehicle must be push-started.
    B. Boost from another vehicle with high-voltage hybrid drive.
    C. The high-voltage battery pack must be slow-charged.
    D. Boost using another 12V-DC source to crank the secondary starter.

83. Rotor resistance is being tested on an alternator by attaching DVOM leads to the A and F terminal screws. Which of the following must be done before performing the test?

    A. Run engine at 1500 rpm.
    B. Remove alternator from the engine.
    C. Disconnect the battery.
    D. Remove the alternator drive belt.

84. A customer complains that the DRL (daylight running lights) on his vehicle switch off when the engine is on and the parking brake actuated. Which of the following is the likely cause?

    A. Short between the DRL and parking brake circuit.
    B. Poor ground at DRL lamp socket.
    C. Intermittent open in the DRL circuit.
    D. Normal condition in some vehicles.

85. The turn signals on a vehicle equipped with dual filament tail-light bulbs flash rapidly when a right turn is signalled. Which of the following would be the more likely cause of this condition?

    A. An open in the right-turn signal circuit.
    B. A dead short to ground in the right-turn circuit.
    C. Feedback connection at the bulb circuit between the turn and tail light terminals.
    D. A failed tail light filament in the right side dual filament bulb.

86. Which of the electrical devices supplies an input signal to the cruise-control electronics?

    A.  Instrument cluster unit.
    B.  Stoplight switch.
    C.  Tail light bulb.
    D.  Turn light switch.

87. Which of the following would be the more likely cause of an HID headlamp failure?

    A.  Failed bulb filament.
    B.  Corroded bulb socket.
    C.  Failed HID control module.
    D.  Burned out electrodes.

88. Source voltage on an automobile with its engine running and headlights switched on, is measured at 13.5 V. If the voltage available at the positive terminal on one of the headlights is measured at 12.7 V, which of the following is correct?

    A.  The charging circuit is defective.
    B.  The headlight circuit is functioning properly.
    C.  The headlight being tested is not properly grounded.
    D.  There is excessive resistance in the insulated side of the headlight circuit.

89. A headlight circuit uses a virtual, cycling circuit breaker. How does this differ from a headlamp circuit that uses a mechanical circuit breaker?

    A.  Virtual circuit breakers must be backup-protected by a fuse.
    B.  Virtual circuit breakers can only handle low-current loads.
    C.  Virtual circuit breakers are more sensitive to voltage dump.
    D.  Virtual circuit breakers have no moving parts.

90. On a standard SAE-coded relay, what is the common terminal coded as?

    A.  1.
    B.  3.
    C.  4.
    D.  5.

91. How many wires are used in the multiplexing backbone used by a CAN 2.0 data bus (J1850), not counting the shield?

    A.  16.
    B.  8.
    C.  2.
    D.  1.

92. When troubleshooting a complaint of insufficient passenger compartment heat during cold weather operation, which of the following possible causes should you check first?

    A. Temperature of upper radiator hose.
    B. Engine thermostat.
    C. Heater core restriction.
    D. Heater control valve operation.

93. Which of the following would be the more costly consequence of using a mineral-based oil in an HFC-134a A/C system?

    A. Reduced system performance.
    B. Contaminated refrigerant.
    C. Compressor failure due to insufficient lubrication.
    D. Passenger compartment odour.

94. What is the appropriate tool for electrically assessing the circuit for the field coils of an A/C compressor clutch?

    A. Voltmeter.
    B. Ammeter.
    C. Diode tester.
    D. Ohmmeter.

95. Under which of the following service procedures would it be acceptable to have both the high and low side hand valves open at the same time?

    A. Evacuating the A/C system.
    B. Recharging with the A/C system running.
    C. Checking for leaks with the A/C system running.
    D. System performance testing with the A/C running.

96. What would result if an HFC-134a A/C system were 25% overcharged with refrigerant during servicing?

    A. Passenger compartment temperatures would be cooler than specified.
    B. The A/C system would operate for 25% longer before next service.
    C. Ester oil becomes permanently contaminated.
    D. The A/C system would operate at lower efficiency.

97. What should prevent refrigerant discharge to atmosphere in the event of a high-pressure service valve leak in an HFC-134a system?

    A. Depressor pin.
    B. O-ring in the service valve cap.
    C. Check engine alert to driver.
    D. None, the refrigerant completely discharges to atmosphere.

## Block F: Steering, Suspension, Braking, and Control Systems

98. A dry park test is typically used to diagnose which of the following components?

    A. Upper strut mount.
    B. Strut bearing.
    C. Inner tie rod.
    D. Power steering pump.

99. When performing steering column service work on a vehicle equipped with an air bag, which of the following should be done first?

    A. Pull the SRS fuse and continue working.
    B. Disconnect both battery cables and wait 20 minutes.
    C. Disconnect the harness to the air bag controller.
    D. Connect yourself to ground with a static strap.

100. Using a spring scale to measure steering wheel turning effort is necessary while performing which of the following?

    A. Toe adjustment.
    B. Tie rod replacement.
    C. Worm bearing preload adjustment.
    D. Intermediate steering shaft replacement.

101. A vehicle with air ride suspension sits too low to the ground but the compressor does work. Which of the following is a likely cause?

    A. Inoperative relay.
    B. High resistance in the height sensor wiring.
    C. Blown fuse.
    D. Inoperative air-exhaust solenoid.

102. A vehicle has a groan through the entire rotation of the steering wheel. Which of the following could be the cause?

    A. Dry strut bearing.
    B. Loose power steering belt.
    C. Low tire pressure.
    D. Steering shaft universal joint.

103. Which of the following could cause a clunk on heavy acceleration or heavy deceleration?

    A. Strut bearings.
    B. Outer tie rod end.
    C. Subframe mounts.
    D. Engine mounts.

104. A customer complains of a low brake pedal. Which of the following is correct?

    A. Air in the system.
    B. Incorrect bleeding procedure used.
    C. Excessive rotor runout.
    D. Seized star wheel.

105. A hard brake pedal is noticed. Which of the following is a likely cause?

    A. Defective master cylinder.
    B. Parking brake stuck partially on.
    C. Open vacuum check valve.
    D. Leaking poppet assembly.

106. What could cause brake fluid to be found on the carpet in a vehicle?

    A. Leaking booster diaphragm.
    B. Broken brake line.
    C. Defective secondary seal on the primary piston.
    D. Reservoir cap missing.

107. During which of the following conditions will a worn left front-sealed bearing generally make noise?

    A. Left turn while accelerating.
    B. Left turn while decelerating.
    C. Right turn while accelerating.
    D. Right turn while decelerating.

108. Which of the following will cause a scalloping wear pattern on a tire?

    A. Weak shock absorbers.
    B. Incorrect caster angle.
    C. Incorrect toe angle.
    D. Shifted belt in tire.

109. Which of the following is a necessary precaution when replacing a pitman arm?

    A. Do not use an air-powered pickle fork.
    B. Never pry against the vehicle frame.
    C. Never heat the pitman arm.
    D. Never use a screw-type puller.

110. When performing a power steering hydraulic pressure test, the test valve should be closed to test which of the following components?

    A. Pump.
    B. Control valve.
    C. Power piston.
    D. Hoses.

111. Which of the following is the correct way to increase caster on a Macpherson strut suspension system equipped with a strut bar?

   A. Rotate the eccentric on the lost strut mount.
   B. Rotate the tie rod counter clockwise.
   C. Adjust the strut bar.
   D. Add shims to the top of the strut.

112. Which of the following adjustments should be performed first during a 4-wheel alignment?

   A. Front caster.
   B. Front camber.
   C. Rear caster.
   D. Rear camber.

113. What alignment angles will determine subframe misalignment?

   A. SAI and camber.
   B. SAI and caster.
   C. Included angle and toe.
   D. Thrust angle and camber.

114. A single clunk noise heard at every brake application may be caused by which of the following?

   A. Dry caliper sliders.
   B. Incorrect clearance between caliper and knuckle.
   C. Weak pad retainer springs.
   D. A rotor with hot spots.

115. After replacing a leaking wheel cylinder assembly and bleeding the system, the red brake warning lamp remains illuminated. Which of the following is a likely cause?

   A. Low brake fluid.
   B. Stuck proportioning valve.
   C. Defective metering valve.
   D. Stuck pressure differential valve.

116. On a metering valve-equipped vehicle, no fluid is present at the front wheels during pressure bleeding. What is the most likely cause?

   A. Collapsed front brake hoses.
   B. Pressure bleeder setting too high.
   C. Pressure bleeder setting too low.
   D. Plugged master cylinder compensating port.

117. A vehicle has an illuminated ABS lamp with a code for Left Front Wheel Erratic (C0227). Which of the following is a likely cause?

    A. Left front wheel speed connector pin tension.
    B. Open wire in left front harness.
    C. Shorted connection in left front harness.
    D. Incorrect sensor gap.

118. Where is the most accurate spot to take wheel runout measurements?

    A. On the outside of the rim lip.
    B. Centre of tire tread.
    C. Inside of wheel rim.
    D. Wheel flange.

119. What can cause a serviceable tapered wheel bearing to have scoring only at one end of the roller?

    A. Lack of lubrication.
    B. Metal fatigue.
    C. High mileage.
    D. Excessive preload.

## Block G: Body Components, Trim, and Restraint Systems

120. When replacing defective air bag system sensors, it is imperative to do which of the following?

    A. Ensure all arrows point forward.
    B. Replace the diagnostic module.
    C. Leave the battery connected.
    D. Reprogram the diagnostic module.

121. A customer complains of a whistling noise at speeds over 60 km/h. Which of the following is a likely cause?

    A. Incorrect hood bumper height.
    B. Loose left side trim moulding.
    C. Incorrect tie rod sleeve placement.
    D. Broken radiator shroud.

122. What is the most effective way of finding water leaks in a passenger compartment?

    A. Trouble light.
    B. Smoke machine.
    C. Electronic stethoscope.
    D. Air nozzle.

123. What could cause all power windows in a vehicle to become inoperative?

    A.   Defective motors.
    B.   Broken wire in right front-door jamb.
    C.   High resistance ground for master switch.
    D.   Malfunctioning express-down circuitry.

124. What is the first thing that should be done with a door that appears to have sagged?

    A.   Loosen lower hinge bolts to adjust door.
    B.   Complete the up-down adjustment before the in-out adjustments.
    C.   Adjust door striker to match door.
    D.   Check for up-down hinge play.

125. Which of the following is the most correct way to repair a broken door jamb wire?

    A.   Solder the connection in the door jamb.
    B.   Use crimp butt connectors in the door jamb.
    C.   Run a new wire through the jamb and connect on both sides.
    D.   Twist the wires together and tape.

# Answer Key to Practice Tests ➤ 8

---

**Answers to Practice Test 1**

| | | | | | | | | | |
|---|---|---|---|---|---|---|---|---|---|
| 1. | B | 31. | C | 61. | C | 91. | A | 121. | C |
| 2. | C | 32. | D | 62. | B | 92. | B | 122. | A |
| 3. | B | 33. | A | 63. | C | 93. | D | 123. | C |
| 4. | C | 34. | B | 64. | B | 94. | C | 124. | D |
| 5. | C | 35. | C | 65. | C | 95. | D | 125. | C |
| 6. | A | 36. | D | 66. | D | 96. | B | | |
| 7. | C | 37. | C | 67. | C | 97. | A | | |
| 8. | B | 38. | A | 68. | A | 98. | C | | |
| 9. | C | 39. | D | 69. | A | 99. | D | | |
| 10. | A | 40. | C | 70. | A | 100. | D | | |
| 11. | C | 41. | A | 71. | A | 101. | B | | |
| 12. | B | 42. | C | 72. | D | 102. | C | | |
| 13. | A | 43. | D | 73. | D | 103. | D | | |
| 14. | D | 44. | B | 74. | C | 104. | D | | |
| 15. | B | 45. | D | 75. | A | 105. | B | | |
| 16. | C | 46. | A | 76. | D | 106. | D | | |
| 17. | D | 47. | B | 77. | A | 107. | B | | |
| 18. | C | 48. | C | 78. | C | 108. | A | | |
| 19. | A | 49. | A | 79. | A | 109. | B | | |
| 20. | C | 50. | B | 80. | D | 110. | D | | |
| 21. | C | 51. | D | 81. | C | 111. | B | | |
| 22. | B | 52. | A | 82. | C | 112. | C | | |
| 23. | A | 53. | B | 83. | A | 113. | B | | |
| 24. | C | 54. | D | 84. | B | 114. | C | | |
| 25. | C | 55. | A | 85. | C | 115. | B | | |
| 26. | A | 56. | C | 86. | D | 116. | B | | |
| 27. | B | 57. | D | 87. | D | 117. | D | | |
| 28. | C | 58. | B | 88. | D | 118. | A | | |
| 29. | C | 59. | C | 89. | B | 119. | C | | |
| 30. | A | 60. | D | 90. | C | 120. | B | | |

## Answers to Practice Test 2

| | | | | | | | | | |
|---|---|---|---|---|---|---|---|---|---|
| 1. | D | 31. | B | 61. | C | 91. | C | 121. | B |
| 2. | B | 32. | C | 62. | B | 92. | C | 122. | B |
| 3. | C | 33. | B | 63. | B | 93. | D | 123. | B |
| 4. | B | 34. | C | 64. | A | 94. | B | 124. | A |
| 5. | C | 35. | B | 65. | C | 95. | B | 125. | D |
| 6. | C | 36. | C | 66. | B | 96. | C | | |
| 7. | B | 37. | A | 67. | C | 97. | A | | |
| 8. | D | 38. | C | 68. | C | 98. | D | | |
| 9. | C | 39. | C | 69. | B | 99. | A | | |
| 10. | A | 40. | A | 70. | C | 100. | C | | |
| 11. | C | 41. | B | 71. | D | 101. | B | | |
| 12. | C | 42. | C | 72. | D | 102. | C | | |
| 13. | A | 43. | D | 73. | C | 103. | C | | |
| 14. | C | 44. | B | 74. | C | 104. | B | | |
| 15. | B | 45. | C | 75. | B | 105. | B | | |
| 16. | B | 46. | A | 76. | B | 106. | B | | |
| 17. | A | 47. | A | 77. | D | 107. | A | | |
| 18. | D | 48. | C | 78. | B | 108. | C | | |
| 19. | B | 49. | D | 79. | B | 109. | C | | |
| 20. | A | 50. | B | 80. | B | 110. | B | | |
| 21. | D | 51. | A | 81. | C | 111. | C | | |
| 22. | D | 52. | B | 82. | D | 112. | C | | |
| 23. | D | 53. | D | 83. | D | 113. | B | | |
| 24. | B | 54. | C | 84. | B | 114. | A | | |
| 25. | D | 55. | C | 85. | D | 115. | B | | |
| 26. | D | 56. | A | 86. | D | 116. | A | | |
| 27. | C | 57. | B | 87. | B | 117. | A | | |
| 28. | B | 58. | D | 88. | C | 118. | C | | |
| 29. | A | 59. | A | 89. | D | 119. | B | | |
| 30. | B | 60. | D | 90. | D | 120. | A | | |

# Answers to Practice Test 3

| | | | | | | | | | |
|---|---|---|---|---|---|---|---|---|---|
| 1. | C | 31. | C | 61. | A | 91. | C | 121. | C |
| 2. | C | 32. | B | 62. | C | 92. | A | 122. | B |
| 3. | D | 33. | C | 63. | A | 93. | C | 123. | C |
| 4. | B | 34. | B | 64. | C | 94. | A | 124. | D |
| 5. | B | 35. | D | 65. | D | 95. | A | 125. | C |
| 6. | A | 36. | C | 66. | C | 96. | D | | |
| 7. | C | 37. | D | 67. | C | 97. | B | | |
| 8. | B | 38. | D | 68. | A | 98. | C | | |
| 9. | A | 39. | B | 69. | C | 99. | B | | |
| 10. | C | 40. | B | 70. | D | 100. | C | | |
| 11. | C | 41. | D | 71. | A | 101. | B | | |
| 12. | A | 42. | A | 72. | C | 102. | A | | |
| 13. | C | 43. | C | 73. | B | 103. | C | | |
| 14. | C | 44. | C | 74. | C | 104. | C | | |
| 15. | B | 45. | A | 75. | C | 105. | D | | |
| 16. | D | 46. | D | 76. | A | 106. | C | | |
| 17. | B | 47. | C | 77. | C | 107. | D | | |
| 18. | D | 48. | A | 78. | A | 108. | A | | |
| 19. | C | 49. | C | 79. | B | 109. | C | | |
| 20. | A | 50. | B | 80. | D | 110. | A | | |
| 21. | C | 51. | A | 81. | C | 111. | C | | |
| 22. | B | 52. | B | 82. | D | 112. | D | | |
| 23. | D | 53. | A | 83. | C | 113. | A | | |
| 24. | C | 54. | D | 84. | D | 114. | B | | |
| 25. | A | 55. | B | 85. | C | 115. | D | | |
| 26. | B | 56. | C | 86. | B | 116. | B | | |
| 27. | C | 57. | A | 87. | D | 117. | A | | |
| 28. | B | 58. | A | 88. | D | 118. | C | | |
| 29. | C | 59. | B | 89. | D | 119. | D | | |
| 30. | B | 60. | D | 90. | B | 120. | A | | |

# Explanations for Practice Test 1 Answers ➤ 9

---

## Block A: Occupational Skills

1. **Answer B is correct.**
   Goggles fitted with a #5 filter lens are required to protect eyes performing torch cutting with oxy-acetylene.

2. **Answer C is correct.**
   Vibration in a hydraulic hoist is usually an indication of an oil leak or low hydraulic fluid level.

3. **Answer B is correct.**
   Only dry powder extinguishing agents can be used on all 4 categories of fire, so most auto shops are equipped with these. Carbon dioxide extinguishers are effective with all but Class-D (flammable metal) category fires, so it also makes sense to have these in a shop environment because they do not produce the mess associated with dry powder.

4. **Answer C is correct.**
   You should know what information is required on an MSDS that must accompany any potentially dangerous product in a workplace in Canada and the US.

5. **Answer C is correct.**
   Following a workplace accident that has resulted in an injury, a WSIB report must be completed.

6. **Answer A is correct.**
   Only CD-ROMs are read optically by a computer; diskettes and the hard drive are both magnetic data retention devices, and microfiche is a nearly obsolete film information retention medium, once popular in the automotive industry.

7. **Answer C is correct.**
   An estimate guide contains both the labour and parts estimates.

8. **Answer B is correct.**

The VIN must be displayed on top of the dash on the driver's side of the vehicle. It may also be displayed in other locations on the vehicle.

9. **Answer C is correct.**

In most Canadian jurisdictions, the actual bill may not exceed the repair estimate by more than 10%.

## Block B: Engine Systems

10. **Answer A is correct.**

When an engine is run without a thermostat, coolant is circulated at a higher rate and it is unlikely the operating temperature will be achieved. This results in lower combustion temperatures that will mean that the fuel is not properly oxidized, increasing both HC and CO emissions.

11. **Answer C is correct.**

A cold, cam-ground piston is slightly oval in shape. It is designed to expand to a perfectly round shape at engine-operating temperatures. Pistons have more mass at the pin boss and when heated, the pin boss expands more; cam-ground pistons compensate for this.

12. **Answer B is correct.**

Plastigage™ strips are used to measure friction-bearing clearance. They are crushed between the journal and the bearing shell, so that when clearance decreases, the strip becomes wider.

13. **Answer A is correct.**

When an interference angle is cut to a valve, it is almost always 1°.

14. **Answer D is correct.**

Crankshaft end play is defined by thrust bearings.

15. **Answer B is correct.**

The correct method of measuring a cylinder head for warpage is to use a straight edge and feeler gauges.

16. **Answer C is correct.**

When a cylinder head valve is equipped with 2 valve springs they are wound oppositely.

17. **Answer D is correct.**

When a full-flow oil filter plugs on sediment, the oil from the oil pump is routed around the filter assembly by a bypass valve.

18. **Answer C is correct.**

When a spark plug fails, raw fuel and oxygen are discharged from the dead cylinder into the exhaust system. The oxygen sensor is designed to read and compare oxygen in the exhaust gas with that in the atmosphere. Because unre-acted oxygen from the dead cylinder is dumped into the exhaust, it signals low voltage (oxygen-rich condition) and the ECM will respond by increasing the fuel load to the engine in an attempt to rectify the condition. This will result in both over-fuelling and a possible overheat condition.

19. **Answer A is correct.**
Pinging, also known as knock, is a detonation condition caused by too rapid a combustion of fuel. A pinging condition that occurs only once the engine has warmed is a symptom of a gasoline that has a low octane rating, often caused by hot weather degradation.

20. **Answer C is correct.**
When the accelerator is depressed for a full power request, vacuum drops off and a vacuum-actuated regulator steps the fuel rail pressure to a higher value.

21. **Answer C is correct.**
When the armature of the injector is energized, the pintle is unseated, allowing rail fuel to pass through the injector to fuel the engine.

22. **Answer B is correct.**
Both the fuel pump check valve and accumulator (on systems equipped with one) function to prevent fuel drainage from the rail when the engine is not being run.

23. **Answer A is correct.**
Stoichiometric fuelling in closed loop should produce an oxygen sensor voltage output of between 0.45 and 0.5 V-DC. If the mixture were richer, the output voltage would be greater (differential increase) and if it were leaner, output voltage would drop (decrease in differential). Because 0.35 is lower than the stoichiometric fuelling window, it indicates lean mixture.

24. **Answer C is correct.**
Fuel pressure in modern sequential port fuel injection systems can run over 60 psi (414 kPa) and over 300 psi (2 MPa) in direct injection systems. Not relieving fuel pressure could cause fuel to be sprayed uncontrollably. This is a safety concern.

25. **Answer C is correct.**
When performing an injector balance test, all the injectors should drop the same amount of fuel pressure when activated for the same amount of time. If a fuel injector has a lower than normal drop, it is reasonable to conclude that the injector is partially plugged.

26. **Answer A is correct.**
When a gasoline fuel injector is grounded, its electrical circuit is completed and the armature is pulled into the coil, beginning fuelling.

27. **Answer B is correct.**
Most gasoline fuel injectors are ground side controlled by the ECM.

## Block C: Vehicle Management Systems

28. **Answer C is correct.**
OBD codes have 5 characters: the 1st identifies the area of the vehicle (power-train, chassis, etc.), the 2nd is an SAE- or OEM-designated code, the 3rd designates the system that is the subject of the code, and the final 2 (4 and 5), the sensor or actuator circuit where the problem has occurred.

29. **Answer C is correct.**
When an exhaust manifold is cracked, air can be pulled into the exhaust gas stream by back pressure. This would cause the oxygen sensor to signal a lean-burn condition to the ECM.

30. **Answer A is correct.**
A MAP (manifold actual pressure) sensor should provide a reading close to atmospheric pressure. Knowing the common acronyms for sensors is important: TP (throttle position), ECT (engine coolant temperature) sensor and TBS (turbo boost sensor) are the distractors in this case.

31. **Answer C is correct.**
When an NTC (negative temperature coefficient) ECT (engine coolant temperature) sensor is subjected to heat, its internal resistance decreases, meaning that a higher voltage value is returned as a signal to the ECM.

32. **Answer D is correct.**
NV-RAM data is retained electronically and it is maintained by a direct connection to the battery during key-off. To dump data in NV-RAM, the circuit feed to the chip must be interrupted and this is achieved whenever the battery is disconnected or the computer reset is depressed.

33. **Answer A is correct.**
The length of time current flows in the primary winding of the coil is known as dwell. It is expressed in degrees of rotation. In a contact point system it is the length of time the points are closed, and in an electronic system it is the time the ignition module allows current flow through the coil primary winding.

34. **Answer B is correct.**
The length of the ceramic insulator is what determines a plug's heat range, so a plug with a longer ceramic insulator runs hotter (longer path to dissipate heat) and one with a shorter insulator, cooler. To remedy a hot plug condition, a plug with a shorter ceramic insulator should be selected.

35. **Answer C is correct.**
When a detonation condition is signaled by the knock sensor, the ECM reacts by retarding ignition timing: the knock sensor permits the ECM to manage ignition with the most advance time possible, optimizing power and fuel economy.

36. **Answer D is correct.**

A 3-light logic probe is constructed so that when the red light (upper) is illuminated a voltage value of 10 volts or higher is indicated, the green light (lower) indicates 4 volts and the yellow light (middle) indicates a changing voltage value.

37. **Answer C is correct.**

In most DIS (distributorless ignition systems) described as waste spark systems, 1 coil for every 2 spark plugs is used (opposite in firing order), both are fired together (one producing no ignition on the exhaust stroke), hence the term *waste spark*.

38. **Answer A is correct.**

When an electronic ignition system "opens" the ignition switching transistor, the ignition primary system "opens" and causes the coil to discharge high voltage as its magnetic field collapses.

39. **Answer D is correct.**

The manufacturer-preferred method of removing a thin layer of carbon buildup on an oxygen sensor would be to run the engine lean (pull vacuum hose) for 2 minutes to heat the sensor. If this fails, the sensor can be removed and heated with a propane torch. A propane torch can also be used to verify oxygen sensor output by connecting to a voltmeter and altering the propane-air mixture.

40. **Answer C is correct.**

The problem described probably relates to the timing advance circuit: most of these pumps use a timing advance piston that can be hydraulically (fuel pressure) or electrically (proportioning solenoid) actuated. Diesel fuel pump servicing is expensive and the manufacturer-recommended troubleshooting must be adhered to before removal.

41. **Answer A is correct.**

A rotary distributor diesel fuel pump must be driven through 1 complete effective cycle (delivering a fuelling pulse to each engine cylinder) per full effective cycle of the engine: in a 4-stroke cycle engine, a full cycle requires 2 complete rotations of the engine. One rotation of the fuel pump to two rotations of the engine translates to one half engine speed.

42. **Answer C is correct.**

When a P0171 code is generated, it is usually an indicator that there is excess air entering the induction system causing all cylinders to be affected. The most likely cause here is a ruptured booster diaphragm, because it would allow air to be drawn in uncontrolled.

43. **Answer D is correct.**

With electronic transmissions, the throttle position signal is necessary to determine shift timing and much more. Older mechanical transmissions had a cable attached to the throttle plate to modify transmission throttle pressure.

44. **Answer B is correct.**

If the motherboard has a slight crack through vibration or collision, it is possible for the computer to function until the connection on the motherboard breaks. This will lead to an internal computer error. This would be like flicking an incandescent lamp when it does not work; the filament reattaches and the lamp illuminates.

45. **Answer D is correct.**

When testing PCM wiring, it is important that the wires, pins, or connectors do not become damaged. Anything that can open a pin or pierce a wire is unacceptable. Acupuncture probes are another term for back probes, and these probes are able to slide between the weather packing and the wire to contact the back of the pin.

46. **Answer A is correct.**

Drivers in on-board computers control actuators. In this case, if there were a driver failure, the only output device listed is the IAC (intake/idle air control). The rest are inputs and do not rely on a driver.

47. **Answer B is correct.**

Most 2-wire magnetic pulse generator harnesses are known as "twisted pair" and have a number of wire twists per foot. This is to ensure that there is no magnetic interference into the wire, especially with a crank sensor. This could lead to a no-start condition or misfire condition. Verify after a fix that the wires have been properly twisted.

48. **Answer C is correct.**

An air bag module can be triggered by static electricity. While working around sensitive electronic equipment including air bag equipment, it is a very good idea to wear a static strap so that any static energy you build up will find its way to ground and not through a sensitive, expensive electronic component.

49. **Answer A is correct.**

Some systems will use the anti-lock sensors and circuitry to determine if there is a rough road condition. Rough roads can alter the signal produced in a crank sensor leading to a false misfire count. If the ABS system or its sensors are malfunctioning (the light was on), it is possible that the rough road detection system was deactivated. This would then lead to the generation of the multiple random misfire code.

50. **Answer B is correct.**

Type B codes require that there be 2 consecutive drive cycles where the fault occurs. If it sees only 1 and then a clear cycle, it resets. Type A codes will illuminate the MIL on the first occurrence.

51. **Answer D is correct.**

The most effective way to test an oxygen sensor fix, or almost any on-board computer fix, is to drive the vehicle through a complete drive cycle. This will ensure all on-board test protocols have been reached and that the system or sensor is operating as designed.

52. **Answer A is correct.**

The body control module and sometimes the instrument panel are responsible for the management of the vehicle network. To save battery power, the system is designed to send a "sleep" signal to the modules to power them down. If this sleep signal is not sent or not received, the module or modules will stay on, drawing electrical current. Some modules like *theft* and *keyless entry* never sleep because they could be used without the ignition being on.

53. **Answer B is correct.**

On advanced climate control systems, the doors, blend, and vent are controlled by the BCM. CAN-controlled systems can forget the position of the stepper motors that control the doors if battery power is lost. The system would then have to go through a relearn procedure, possibly with the use of factory scan tools and software.

54. **Answer D is correct.**

Even after the vehicle has gone to production, updates become available for the on-board computers program. Ensure that you have the most up-to-date software to eliminate any "bugs" that the manufacturer has found since the vehicle was produced.

## Block D: Drive Line Systems

55. **Answer A is correct.**

Only half a litre of ATF is required to take an automatic transaxle from ADD to FULL when the unit is hot; typically, the same transmission would require 1 litre to take it from ADD to FULL when cold.

56. **Answer C is correct.**

Overdrive means a speed increase and torque reduction from input. In a simple planetary gearset, this is achieved by using the carrier as the input, holding the ring gear, and outputting through the sun gear.

57. **Answer D is correct.**

There are a number of causes of slippage during shifting. Given that the fluid level and condition check out okay, the best answer would be band adjustment.

58. **Answer B is correct.**

When pressure testing a typical automatic transmission on a road test, the maximum acceptable drop-off between shifts would be 15 psi or 100 kPa.

59. **Answer C is correct.**

Metal particles in transmission fluid tend to be caused by wear of metal components, while dark particles are usually the result of clutch or band wear debris.

60. **Answer D is correct.**

A problem with the transmission is indicated when a 5-second stall test results in engine rpm rising above specification. Always use manufacturer's specifications when performing a stall test, and remember, many late-model vehicles with electronically controlled transmissions cannot be stall tested without damaging the transmission.

61. **Answer C is correct.**

The most accurate method of correcting a driveshaft vibration on a rear-wheel drive vehicle is by using a transducer and strobe light. When a customer is paying for the repair, it is the only method that should be used because of the trial-and-error nature of any other repair method.

62. **Answer B is correct.**

When a clutch is engaged (pedal up), the pressure plate clamps the friction disc to the flywheel, meaning that the clutch assembly rotates at engine speed.

63. **Answer C is correct.**

When a manual transmission jumps out of gear, one of the first things to check would be the detent assemblies, each consisting of a ball and spring responsible for locating the shift rails.

64. **Answer B is correct.**

A plunge CV joint is located on the inboard of the driveshaft assembly; it permits both linear (plunge) and angular movement, unlike the outboard CV joint which permits only angular variations caused by suspension movement.

65. **Answer C is correct.**

When a manual clutch is disengaged on a stationary vehicle with the engine running, the clutch pressure plate, pilot bearing and flywheel are all rotating. The clutch pressure plate is splined to the transmission input (clutch) shaft, so if the vehicle is not moving, this should be stationary.

66. **Answer D is correct.**

Clutch drag is usually caused by a defective release lever, loose friction disc facings, improper pedal/linkage adjustment and warped friction or pressure plates. In this question, the correct answer has to be warped pressure plate.

67. **Answer C is correct.**

The function of a pilot shaft when installing a new clutch assembly is to align the friction disc splines with the pilot bearing so that the transmission input shaft can be easily inserted into the assembly.

68. **Answer A is correct.**

Worn differential pinion-bearing gears could cause a drive axle to be noisy on turns but to be otherwise quiet.

69. **Answer A is correct.**
Constant velocity joints could be found in all of the applications listed except rear-wheel drive vehicles.

70. **Answer A is correct.**
Shims are used to set the depth of mesh of the drive pinion into the ring gear in a final drive unit.

71. **Answer A is correct.**
A full-floating drive shaft is responsible for imparting torque to the wheel assembly and supports none of the vehicle weight.

72. **Answer D is correct.**
When a final drive unit produces a howling noise, the first thing to check is the lubricant level: if low it should be topped up and road-tested. If the howling persists, then the unit should be pulled for overhaul.

## Block E: Electrical and Comfort Control Systems

73. **Answer D is correct.**
A 100% charged lead acid battery should produce a specific gravity reading of + 1.265 at 20°C (68°F).

74. **Answer C is correct.**
The voltage drop test is the only means of accurately locating high resistance in an electrical circuit because the circuit is energized during the test with the normal voltage used in the circuit. Using an ohmmeter requires testing on an open circuit and is not accurate because of the low voltage used for the test from the meter.

75. **Answer A is correct.**
The correct sequence for jump-starting connections should be:
1. Connect positive cable to dead vehicle battery.
2. Connect positive cable to running vehicle battery.
3. Connect ground cable to running vehicle battery.
4. Connect ground cable to dead vehicle engine block.

Note that it is important that the vehicles do not touch during the procedure.

76. **Answer D is correct.**
A defective neutral safety switch could cause a fail-to-crank condition while allowing the headlamps to remain bright. All the other options would dim the lights while attempting to crank the engine.

77. **Answer A is correct.**
The key to answering a question such as this is to read all of the answer options. The conditions described in all 4 possible answers could result in an engine that does not crank and dims the headlamps when the ignition circuit is closed. The

key is the word FIRST. Checking the battery state of charge should be the first step in the troubleshooting sequence.

78. **Answer C is correct.**

    To check starter current draw, engine start should be disabled and the engine cranked while observing current draw. Typical maximum specifications would be 150 amps for 4-cylinder, 200 amps for most V6 and V8, with some V8s maxing at 250 amps.

79. **Answer A is correct.**

    The usual maximum specified voltage drop for any given wire or connection on an alternator is 0.2 V-DC, with 0.5 V-DC being the maximum voltage drop permitted for the circuit.

80. **Answer D is correct.**

    A poorly grounded voltage regulator would likely result in excessively high-charging voltage.

81. **Answer C is correct.**

    When battery voltage is directly applied to the field terminals, the alternator is said to be "full-fielded." The regulator would normally control the field current. If the alternator starts producing when full-fielded, the regulator or regulation system is faulty. If the alternator does not produce when full-fielded, a problem exists in the rotor or stator and bench testing must be done to correctly find the defective component.

82. **Answer C is correct.**

    If any 2 stator windings read infinity when tested with an ohmmeter, the stator is open and defective and should be replaced.

83. **Answer A is correct.**

    The carbon pile tester is used simply to load the battery during an alternator current output test, so the clamps should be located on battery positive and battery or chassis ground for the test. Placing the clamps on light-load terminals could damage wiring and components.

84. **Answer B is correct.**

    Testing for a suspected key-off current drain problem can be done with an ohmmeter by disconnecting the main positive cable and checking the resistance between it and ground. A resistance of 100 ohms or less can drain a battery: Ohm's law can be used to calculate the current drain—for instance, a measurement of 100 ohms would result in a current drain of 0.126 amps assuming a battery voltage of 12.6 V.

85. **Answer C is correct.**

    Body computers control the non-engine functions of the vehicle, and in vehicles that use an electronically controlled dash, a door handle or door jamb switch alerts the body computer of an imminent start-up. The wake-up initiates power supply and circuit-prepare logic for electronic subsystems such as dash display, climate control and the engine: a defective wake-up switch can prevent or delay activation of other on-board electronic systems.

86. **Answer D is correct.**
The headlamp ground integrity should be checked first; dim lights are usually a symptom of a grounding problem.

87. **Answer D is correct.**
Refrigerant must enter the compressor as a low-pressure gas (liquid refrigerant is not compressible). It is then pressurized by the compressor and leaves as a high-pressure gas.

88. **Answer D is correct.**
PAG (polyalkaline glycol) is used in most HFC-134a A/C systems but ester oil can be used in original R-12 systems retrofitted for HFC-134a.

89. **Answer B is correct.**
Refrigerant is boiled from a low-pressure liquid to a low-pressure gas in the evaporator prior to being routed to the accumulator/drier and the compressor.

90. **Answer C is correct.**
The normal operating position of a 3-position stem valve is back-seated. Mid-position is used for testing and front-seated is used to isolate the compressor, allowing it to be serviced without discharging the system.

91. **Answer A is correct.**
When evacuating an HFC-134a A/C system, vacuum should be drawn down to 29.9" of Hg (mercury) and held for at least 30 minutes.

92. **Answer B is correct.**
An electronic leak detector is easily the most sensitive refrigerant leak detector—so much so that it may be difficult to pinpoint larger leaks, so there is even a place for soapy water in testing an A/C system.

93. **Answer D is correct.**
Faster than normal clutch switch cycling is a sure indication of low-refrigerant charge in an HFC-134a A/C system.

94. **Answer C is correct.**
The blend control door determines whether ventilation air flows through the heater core in a typical auto HVAC system.

95. **Answer D is correct.**
Safety glasses should ALWAYS be worn when handling batteries, whether connected into a circuit or not.

96. **Answer B is correct.**
Baking soda and water solution would do the best job of safely neutralizing battery acid. Water will also neutralize acid as will caustic soda, but the latter will

react with the acid and produce hazardous fumes. Petroleum solvents should not be used near battery acid.

97. **Answer A is correct.**
Using a hand-held lab scope on a road test is an accurate, dynamic method of testing the operation of electronically controlled, automatic transmissions solenoid valves because this instrument can display the PWM (pulse width modulated) actuation signals.

# Block F: Steering, Suspension, Braking, and Control Systems

98. **Answer C is correct.**
When bleeding brakes using a pressure or bleeder ball, the metering valve must be held open. This is not required when manually bleeding the brakes.

99. **Answer D is correct.**
Radial wobble or runout of a disc brake rotor is expressed as a TIR (total indicated runout) specification: it is measured by placing the plunger of a dial indicator on the rotor as it is turned through a revolution.

100. **Answer D is correct.**
To measure rotor TIR, the dial indicator should be set at zero and the rotor turned through a complete revolution: the maximum positive measurement is ADDED to the maximum negative measurement.

101. **Answer B is correct.**
Rotor parallelism is measured with an outside micrometer.

102. **Answer C is correct.**
This condition would be caused by brake fluid leaking by a primary cup.

103. **Answer D is correct.**
Repeated braking during a long downhill gradient would heat up both the friction facings and drum, lowering the coefficient of friction of both. Lowering the coefficient of friction makes brakes less aggressive and causes brake fade.

104. **Answer D is correct.**
Worn friction facings, aerated or contaminated brake fluid would be less likely to produce the increased pedal effort described than a power assist malfunction.

105. **Answer B is correct.**
Some ABS hydraulic circuits operate at high pressures maintained by an accumulator that must be relieved of pressure prior to servicing them. Depressing the brake pedal repeatedly with the engine off will effectively lower this pressure.

106. **Answer D is correct.**
While all of the possible answers would produce brake performance problems, pedal pulsation would most likely be caused by a warped rotor.

107. **Answer B is correct.**

Wheel speed sensors induce an AC signal that alters in frequency as rotational speed is changed so their operation can be verified by raising and spinning the wheel and measuring output with a DVOM set on AC voltage. Some manufacturers give specifications for testing wheel speed sensors by measuring resistance across the terminals, but you would not be testing the output of the device.

108. **Answer A is correct.**

When skimming disc brake rotors, between 0.005" (0.13 mm) and 0.010" (0.25 mm) should be removed at each rough cut and no more than 0.002" (0.05 mm) for a finish cut.

109. **Answer B is correct.**

A dual chamber spring brake assembly is divided into service and park/emergency functions. Air pressure is used to hold off a power spring in the spring brake chamber to permit the vehicle to move, while air is supplied to the service chamber for the running brake requirements of the vehicle. To put the vehicle into a park/emergency mode, air is exhausted from the hold-off chamber permitting the power spring to apply the brakes. The force used to park the vehicle is therefore spring force.

110. **Answer D is correct.**

Automatic traction control or electronic traction control uses the brake system to prevent wheel spinout by measuring the relative velocity of each wheel and using the brake system to prevent a spinout condition.

111. **Answer B is correct.**

A feathering bias toward the outside of the tire is usually caused by excessive toe-in: this is created by the scuff action as the tire moves down the road when not geometrically aligned.

112. **Answer C is correct.**

When a tire is under-inflated, wear will be most noticeable on the outside edges of a tire: note that Goodyear states that a 4 psi (28 kPa) under-inflation condition can result in a 10% loss of tread life.

113. **Answer B is correct.**

The maximum pressure an automobile tire can be inflated to when attempting to seat a bead into the rim is usually regarded as 50 psi (345 kPa). Never introduce a flammable substance such as ether to seat a bead as a tire may explode and cause injury.

114. **Answer C is correct.**

An on-the-car spin balancer (single plane or kinetic balance) provides the most precision when balancing a tire because in effect the tire, wheel and rotor are all spun and balanced.

115. **Answer B is correct.**

Removing the valve core during initial inflation will maximize air flow through the Schrader valve body and help seat the bead. Some tire service machines have an integral inflation chamber; this provides a large volume of air for initial inflation.

116. **Answer B is correct.**

A rack-and-pinion steering gear tends to wear in the middle—that is, over centre.

117. **Answer D is correct.**

Steering rack preload adjustment should not be performed when the rack is known to be worn over high point because almost certainly the adjustment will result in binding on turns due to the fact that most wear takes place in the centre.

118. **Answer A is correct.**

Of the 5 alignment angles the 3 normally adjustable angles on a modern automobile are caster, camber, and toe.

119. **Answer C is correct.**

When performing a 4-wheel computer alignment, the steering wheel should be in the straight ahead position. You should know that toe is adjusted on all 4 wheels, that alignment gauges are installed on all 4 wheels, and that thrust angle is calculated factoring the orientation of both front and rear wheels.

## Block G: Body Components, Trim, and Restraint Systems

120. **Answer B is correct.**

A backup capacitor is used to activate an SRS air bag in the event the vehicle battery is destroyed on impact. When the SRS circuit is closed on start-up, the SRS dash light is extinguished when the backup capacitor is charged.

121. **Answer C is correct.**

When an active seat belt system is used, it is mandatory to have a dash alert when a seat belt is not fastened.

122. **Answer A is correct.**

Only ABS group plastics will give off dense black smoke when ignited: if attempting to identify a plastic, break off a small piece, ignite, and avoid inhaling the fumes as it burns. Polypropylene burns giving off little visible smoke; vinyl and nylon emit little smoke and burn with a bluish flame.

123. **Answer C is correct.**

A blown fuse and open circuit would produce the same result, an electrically inoperative wiper/washer circuit, while a sticking ratchet wheel would produce a mechanically inoperative wiper. The first thing to check when a washer runs continuously any time wipers are actuated would be the switch.

124. **Answer D is correct.**

When pulling a steering wheel fitted with an air bag, the air bag wiring harness must be disconnected. Simply disconnecting the battery is not sufficient because the backup capacitor is capable of deploying the air bag.

125. **Answer C is correct.**

According to Ohm's law, when more devices are connected in parallel, the resulting circuit current flow increases as the resistance decreases. If a trailer socket is shorted, the increase in current when activated is likely to burn the fuse. The fuse would not fail when the trailer is not installed because the fault is in the trailer only.

# Explanations for Practice Test 2 Answers ➤ 10

## Block A: Occupational Skills

1. **Answer D is correct.**
   Asbestos dust inhalation is dangerous, so using any method that introduces asbestos dust into the air should be avoided. Use of a CSA-approved filter mask reduces the risk to the technician.

2. **Answer B is correct.**
   To prevent drill bit "walking," a centre punch is necessary to make a small impression where the hole is to be drilled. This will allow the drill to stay in the correct place and not damage any material by "walking" around the intended drill hole location.

3. **Answer C is correct.**
   There are 9 mandatory requirements on every material safety data sheet.

4. **Answer B is correct.**
   When extinguishing a fire, you need to aim the nozzle at the base of the fire to quench the fuel, or nucleus, of the fire. Extinguishing the airborne flames will not quench the root of the fire.

5. **Answer C is correct.**
   Solvents and combustible materials in a shop need to be clearly marked in ventilated storage cabinets away from common areas of work to reduce the risk of accident.

6. **Answer C is correct.**
   If an air-hydraulic hoist bounces or jerks near full extension, there is more than likely air in the hydraulic system. The hydraulic system is not at its full capacity and needs to be replenished and then checked for leakage.

7. **Answer B is correct.**
   It is never acceptable to strike a hammer with another hammer. Hammers generally are made of hardened steel and could easily chip and cause an injury.

8. **Answer D is correct.**

A loud high-pitched squealing sound is the result of a flashback and the correct action is to shut the torch off.

9. **Answer C is correct.**

For best safety cutting and safety results, a cold chisel should be sharpened to 60°.

# Block B: Engine Systems

10. **Answer A is correct.**

The owner is responsible for the maintenance and safety of the vehicle because it is his or her property. Emission control maintenance is the sole responsibility of the vehicle owner.

11. **Answer C is correct.**

Since ethylene glycol, or antifreeze, is toxic and harmful if ingested, it is a legal requirement that recovered engine coolant be sent to a recycling operation and there disposed of or remanufactured properly.

12. **Answer C is correct.**

Oil should never be washed down a drain. It should be absorbed, swept up, and disposed of with an oil recycling company. This prevents any environmental infractions for pollution.

13. **Answer A is correct.**

The radiator cap is designed to allow coolant out to the overflow tank if the cooling system pressure exceeds the cap pressure rating. The radiator cap also permits coolant to return to the cooling system as it cools and the pressure drops. If the radiator cap does not allow coolant to be drawn back into the cooling system, low pressure occurs and radiator hoses can collapse.

14. **Answer C is correct.**

A seized-closed wastegate would route all the exhaust through the turbine. This would keep manifold boost pressures high to the point where engine knocking could occur.

15. **Answer B is correct.**

If an oil pressure regulator is stuck closed, excess pressure generated by the oil pump is not regulated, meaning that it is routed into the oil lubrication circuit rather than cycled back to the oil pan.

16. **Answer B is correct.**

To check piston ring groove wear, you must install a new piston ring and insert a feeler gauge between the upper surface of the ring and the land. If the ring groove is out of specification, a new piston or a piston repair is required.

17. **Answer A is correct.**

When reinstalling an engine, if the transmission bell housing is torqued improperly, it can cause the bell housing to distort. Most transmission bell housings are made of aluminum.

18. **Answer D is correct.**

A piston pin will make a knocking noise that will not disappear when the spark plug to that cylinder is grounded out.

19. **Answer B is correct.**

Debris in the radiator fins blocks the flow of air through the radiator. The problem is more likely to occur in stop-and-go traffic because the airflow is greatly reduced. The electric or clutch fan cannot flow as much air as the ram air effect of a travelling vehicle.

20. **Answer A is correct.**

Align boring a cylinder block should be performed before any other procedure.

21. **Answer D is correct.**

The PCM controls the prime cycle of the electric fuel pump. Because the prime cycle takes place, this confirms that both the PCM and fuel pump relay are operational. However, if the PCM does not receive a valid signal from the crankshaft position sensor, it will not actuate the fuel pump following the prime cycle.

22. **Answer D is correct.**

Even though a broken vacuum line to the regulator will cause higher than normal fuel pressures at wide open throttle, the vacuum will be essentially zero, making fuel pressure high but within the normal range. A restricted return line will cause excessive fuel pressure well outside the normal range.

23. **Answer D is correct.**

Before condemning the fuel pump because of low pressure, it is necessary to check dynamic pressure at the fuel pump, before testing other components such as transfer pumps and fuel filters. Good pressure at the pump indicates a restriction in the line downstream from the fuel pump.

24. **Answer B is correct.**

It is unlikely that both injectors develop excessive resistance to ground at the same time, so if there is spark and good TPS voltage, a burned fuse will result in no visible injector pulse with a noid light.

25. **Answer D is correct.**

A port fuel injected vehicle will have the highest fuel pressure when the throttle is depressed to 100%. If the vehicle is equipped with a vacuum regulator, engine vacuum drops to zero inHg when at wide-open throttle or 100%. A vacuum regulator with no vacuum will cause higher fuel pressure.

26. **Answer D is correct.**

Since there is no audible noise from the injector, the armature is not moving within the injector, making a seized armature likely.

27. **Answer C is correct.**

The fuel pressure regulator on a no-return circuit system is in the fuel tank. Since the MAP sensor measures manifold vacuum, its signal can be used to electronically regulate the fuel, rather than a vacuum-operated diaphragm.

## Block C: Vehicle Management Systems

28. **Answer B is correct.**

The lower injector seal in a sequential port, gasoline fuel injection system is a seal between atmosphere and the intake manifold. A leaking lower injector seal will therefore allow unmetered air into the intake causing a leaner air-fuel mixture.

29. **Answer A is correct.**

A flashing MIL indicates that there is an engine misfire that at the current engine speed and load conditions could cause catalytic converter damage.

30. **Answer B is correct.**

A STFT number of –10% indicates that the PCM, on signal information from the oxygen sensor, is operating in closed loop, and is subtracting fuel out of the mixture to lean the AFR.

31. **Answer B is correct.**

If the PCM reads throttle position as being wide open, the PCM shuts off the injector pulse and goes into "clear flood" mode. A shorted signal wire to 5 volts would signal the PCM that the throttle was wide open.

32. **Answer C is correct.**

A magnetic pulse generator would typically produce 1–2 V-AC during cranking.

33. **Answer B is correct.**

The VAF measures airflow via a swing door connected to a potentiometer. The position of the swing door directly relates to the flow of air. With the engine off, the voltage should be low, or close to zero. A reading of 2.6 V indicates that the plate is open. Checking for binding would be a good first test.

34. **Answer C is correct.**

All of the ignition triggering devices produce a digital or on/off output except the magnetic pulse generator, the magnetic triggering device that produces an AC signal.

35. **Answer B is correct.**

A shorted spark plug will produce an abnormally low firing line. Because there is a shorter path for the spark to cross, less firing or ionizing voltage is required.

36. **Answer C is correct.**

Because a misfire results in incomplete or no combustion in a cylinder, raw oxygen is discharged into the exhaust gas. This excess oxygen is read by the oxygen sensor as a lean condition and it will signal a lower voltage value.

37. **Answer A is correct.**

As engine speed increases, ignition timing must advance to allow combustion to take place while the piston is in an appropriate position through the power stroke. As engine speed increases, the real time available for combustion proportionally decreases.

38. **Answer C is correct.**

A functioning oxygen sensor will produce approximately 1–5 cross-counts per second. Although the number values are correct, the best determination is made by viewing a graph output of the oxygen sensor cross-counts.

39. **Answer C is correct.**

The spark line is the voltage that is required to sustain the spark after the initial ionization. A partially open EGR valve will cause turbulence in the combustion chamber that will result in a "lumpy" or oscillating spark line on all cylinders.

40. **Answer A is correct.**

A mechanical engine knock will be interpreted by the engine knock sensor as "pinging" or spark knock. When the PCM sees this signal, it will retard the timing. Since the source of the trouble is not timing but is engine mechanics-related, the vehicle will lack power and become sluggish.

41. **Answer B is correct.**

A leaking injector nozzle can cause a diesel engine to run rough and result in smoking due to improperly combusted fuel.

42. **Answer C is correct.**

Since the sensor is disconnected, the live data should show approximately 450 mV. With zero volts returning between the sensor connector and the PCM, the signal wire is more than likely shorted to ground.

43. **Answer D is correct.**

If the fuel pressure is too high, excess fuel will be present in the combustion chamber. This means that in combustion, all of the oxygen is consumed and less oxygen is detected in the exhaust gas by the oxygen sensor. This results in the oxygen sensor signaling higher voltage, indicating rich AFR.

44. **Answer B is correct.**

The anatomy of an OBD II code is as such: the 1st letter refers to the system where the malfunction is. In this case it is P—powertrain. The 2nd digit refers to whether or not it is a generic or manufacturer-specific code. (1—Manufacturer, 0—SAE.) The 3rd digit refers to the subsystem where the fault lies. In this case, the idle control circuit is under section 5—Vehicle Speed, Idle Control and Auxiliary Inputs. The actual code P0505 signifies Idle Control System

Malfunction. C codes represent chassis systems, B codes represent body systems, and U codes represent network system malfunctions.

45. **Answer C is correct.**
During the first 2 1/2 minutes of idling after a start, the PCM will have the ability to check the canister purge system, oxygen sensor heater, fuel trim and time to closed loop. The oxygen sensor(s) and catalytic converter(s) will be tested later because they require heat to work efficiently. The EGR system is inactive until load is determined, so the EGR system will be tested during acceleration and cruise routines.

46. **Answer A is correct.**
Newer OBD II systems are built with a communications protocol called Controller Area Network (CAN), also known as J1850. If the vehicle has CAN communications network, it may not be able to communicate with older scan tools without the aid of an adapter to translate the information. CAN adapters are available through major automotive diagnostic tool suppliers.

47. **Answer A is correct.**
The service manual contains information on codes as well as the trouble trees to effectively diagnose on-board faults. These trees usually employ strategy-based diagnostic principles and need to be adhered to in order to find the fault in the best possible way.

48. **Answer C is correct.**
Power window circuitry is part of the body systems, and therefore, in order to find data on power window systems, you would need to look in the BCM.

49. **Answer D is correct.**
Diagnosing U codes, or network codes, requires the use of a high-speed lab scope. The information on the serial data line is a series of pulses that are a message to another controller. If there is an intermittent in the line, monitor the lab scope while tracing the wires to find a broken connection. The code U0029 signifies Vehicle Communication Bus A Performance.

50. **Answer B is correct.**
To properly change a pin connection in harness connector, you should always use the correct terminal tool in order to prevent damage to the connector or harness itself. Splayed terminals are usually caused by inappropriate test equipment opening the terminal. This will cause a poor connection between male and female connectors and can lead to intermittent problems and difficult diagnosing.

51. **Answer A is correct.**
The PCM in an OBD II-compliant vehicle is designed to illuminate a malfunction indicator lamp if there is a possibility that the occurring fault could raise the tailpipe emissions by 1 1/2 times the federal test procedure standard. Thus, if the emissions are going to be 50% higher, there should be an illuminated MIL.

52. **Answer B is correct.**

To properly run all readiness tests or drive cycle, the coolant temperature or ECT should be less than 50°C (122°F) and have the IAT (intake air temperature) sensor within 6°C (11°F). This will allow for warm-up tests in the cycle to be run.

53. **Answer D is correct.**

Active suspension is part of the chassis system. The first letter in an OBD II code signifies the system where the fault is occurring. P—Powertrain, B—Body, C—Chassis, U—Network. The code for an active suspension fault would start with the letter C.

54. **Answer C is correct.**

The oxygen sensor (HO2S) is allowed to cool when the vehicle is turned off as the hot exhaust gases stop flowing. Upon restart, the oxygen sensor warms and the system is in open loop. If the oxygen sensor malfunctions and provides false information, when the system changes to closed loop, fuel control is based on oxygen sensor reading. This can severely alter fuel deliver and cause a harsh hesitation.

# Block D: Drive Line Systems

55. **Answer C is correct.**

Milky transmission oil is usually caused by coolant mixing with transmission oil. Because most automatic transmissions have an oil cooler integral with the radiator, a ruptured cooler is the most likely cause.

56. **Answer A is correct.**

Most electronically controlled transmissions have a limp-home mode that defaults the transmission into 3rd gear regardless of gear selector position when a serious transmission problem occurs. This permits the vehicle to be driven, albeit with some difficulty, and to be repaired without having to resort to towing.

57. **Answer B is correct.**

A stuck-closed lock-up solenoid will not allow the torque converter to uncouple the transmission from the engine, causing an effect like a manual clutch that will not disengage.

58. **Answer D is correct.**

A misadjusted kick-down cable can cause a delayed upshift as the throttle pressure will be interrupted as if in a lower gear.

59. **Answer A is correct.**

While air testing an automatic transmission, clunking indicates the servo is successfully engaging the bands. Hissing, however, is an indicator of a leaking servo diaphragm, so this conclusion is correct.

60. **Answer D is correct.**
Because the torque converter is usually a sealed component, the inspection should be confined to checking the flex plate to the torque converter bolts to ensure a tight connection.

61. **Answer C is correct.**
If the carrier is the input, the output will always be overdrive.

62. **Answer B is correct.**
Most manufacturers will provide a quill sleeve to place over the transmission input shaft sleeve at the point where the release bearing rides. This will eliminate the need for transmission overhaul when replacing a clutch and/or release bearing.

63. **Answer B is correct.**
Hard shifting will result if there is improper lubrication in the manual transaxle. The synchronizers require lubrication for proper operation.

64. **Answer A is correct.**
When the clutch is engaged, the transaxle input shaft bearings are moving. A growling noise will be present if the bearings have failed.

65. **Answer C is correct.**
Air in the slave cylinder of a hydraulic clutch system will cause poor clutch release because the air will compress, not allowing the hydraulic fluid to actuate the slave piston. If the slave piston does not move far enough, the clutch will not release properly.

66. **Answer B is correct.**
A dragging clutch is common to all gears. If the clash occurs in all gears, the clutch may not be fully releasing when changing gears.

67. **Answer C is correct.**
The pilot bearing needs to be lightly lubricated with a high-temperature grease to provide lubrication in a generally non-accessible part.

68. **Answer C is correct.**
If the pinion depth is less than specification, the wear will occur at the toe of the teeth.

69. **Answer B is correct.**
Improper driveline angles can be corrected by changing or shimming engine, transmission, and rear axle mounts. Installing wedges at the rear axle will change the driveline angle.

70. **Answer C is correct.**
Since the weight transfer while turning right is to the left, the damaged CV joint is probably the outboard joint on the left side.

71. **Answer D is correct.**

If ring gear backlash is improperly adjusted, the gears will whine and produce clunking noises while in operation.

72. **Answer D is correct.**

The pinion and side gear thrust washers are designed to move slightly to accommodate turning. If a wheel is allowed to spin out (snow or ice) for a period of time, the gears can overheat and damage the thrust washers because they are rotating at speeds they were not engineered for.

# Block E: Electrical and Comfort Control Systems

73. **Answer C is correct.**

Because the variation between the specific gravity in the two cells is greater than 0.050 on a fully charged battery, the battery needs to be replaced.

74. **Answer C is correct.**

A defective or marred flywheel will cause an imperfect fit between the starter pinion gear and the flywheel ring gear teeth. The result of this irregular gear mesh can be a whine while the gears are in mesh.

75. **Answer B is correct.**

On a shimable starter, the clearance between the flywheel and the starter drive shaft is specified at 1/8" (3.18 mm).

76. **Answer B is correct.**

Worn starter bushings can cause the starter armature to dig into the pole shoes and bind. If the bushings are worn severely, the starter may fail to turn over.

77. **Answer D is correct.**

If the starter has corrosion or high resistance in the ground circuit (that is, the mounting flange between the starter and the transmission or engine), there will be a voltage drop through ground. This voltage drop can result in a no-crank condition.

78. **Answer B is correct.**

The alternator produces AC voltage and the diodes rectify the AC voltage into DC voltage. Rectification leaves a small AC voltage component above the DC voltage line known as AC leakage. Maximum specified AC voltage leakage should be between 0.1–0.5 V-AC. Higher leakage values indicate imminent failure of the diode bridge.

79. **Answer B is correct.**

Excessive alternator whine can be caused by defective diodes. The AC cycling through the defective diodes causes an audible whine.

80. **Answer B is correct.**

The carbon pile is used to place a load on the electrical system to stimulate charging output. The voltage regulator should compensate for the voltage drop and increase alternator output.

81. **Answer C is correct.**

The slip rings and the rotor shaft should have infinite resistance. A reading of 1 ohm indicates that there is a short between the coil windings and the rotor shaft or ground.

82. **Answer D is correct.**

If a vehicle is equipped with a remote starter, the hood pin switch is a safety input to ensure that the vehicle will not start with the hood up. Because the vehicle starts with the key, the switch and wiring are functioning normally. The remote system will not start the vehicle due to the shorted pin switch.

83. **Answer D is correct.**

The radio gets its vehicle speed sensor signal through the PCM and uses this to determine volume. If the vehicle speed sensor or wiring to the PCM were open, the check engine lamp would illuminate and the radio complaint would be dismissed. If the connection were open between the radio and the PCM, the radio microprocessor would be unable to make a volume adjustment based on road speed.

84. **Answer B is correct.**

It is important that the battery be disconnected while handling air bag systems. Failure to do so could result in accidental deployment and possible injury.

85. **Answer D is correct.**

Installing a capacitor is one way to eliminate RFI (radio frequency interference). Since the alternator is an electromagnetic device, a capacitor placed at the output can absorb and cancel RFI.

86. **Answer D is correct.**

Reading 12 volts on both sides of the bulb indicates that the circuit is functional on the positive side and through the bulb. A closed circuit should drop all of the voltage across the load/bulb and read zero on the ground side. An open or incomplete ground circuit will cause this problem.

87. **Answer B is correct.**

An ohmmeter is commonly used to check the resistance of the compressor clutch coil. It is useful to see if the coil is shorted to the housing as well as being electrically open or shorted to itself.

88. **Answer C is correct.**

The condenser condenses the high-pressure vapour into a high-pressure liquid by effectively cooling vapourized refrigerant.

89. **Answer D is correct.**
The service fittings are the only items that must be changed when retrofitting an HFC-134a system to an R-12 system. Retrofit oils are available, and retrofit suppliers claim that even the system seals do not need changing.

90. **Answer D is correct.**
A sight glass is useful in determining an undercharged condition by the presence of bubbles. A charged or completely empty system will not be easily seen in a sight glass.

91. **Answer C is correct.**
The heater door that controls the dash and floor vents is most likely seized or binding to cause venting to the floor only.

92. **Answer C is correct.**
A partially plugged orifice tube will cause rapid cycling of the air-conditioning system and rapid cycling of the low-side pressure due to the extra restriction that is not designed for the system. The low side obtains a lower pressure quicker than normal.

93. **Answer D is correct.**
A pressure sensitive switch manages the compressor clutch on or off to control the flow of refrigerant. In the orifice tube system, the orifice is a fixed calibrated size.

94. **Answer B is correct.**
Clear water is an indicator of either condensation or rainwater. The most likely cause is a plugged heater box drain that cannot dispense the condensation produced as a result of the air-conditioning system.

95. **Answer B is correct.**
An improper air gap could cause wheel speed signal problems to the EBCM. The sensor may be electrically okay, but if the air gap is greater than specification, the sensor voltage signal can be too low to process.

96. **Answer C is correct.**
Using the power equation $P = I \times E$. Therefore, if two 120W lamps are being installed on a 15V system, by the formula, there is a current of 16 amps. (240 = 15 x 16.) Fuses are to be installed where the working current of the system is not to exceed 80% of the fuse rating. Therefore if 16 amps is equal to the 80% rule, then 20 amps is 100%.

97. **Answer A is correct.**
When installing any long cable that runs through the firewall or body, it is imperative that the fusing be done within 12" (30 cm) of the battery to ensure proper protection. Because the connection is direct to the battery, if there were a short to ground along the line and the fuse was in the trunk, melting or fire could result.

# Block F: Steering, Suspension, Braking, and Control Systems

98. **Answer D is correct.**

   The brake warning lamp is most likely illuminated by a broken parking brake pedal return spring that does not allow the signal switch to open.

99. **Answer A is correct.**

   With no fluid spurting out from the compensation port, the piston is returning insufficiently in the master cylinder bore to uncover the compensating port. The brake pedal pushrod adjustment should be looked at first.

100. **Answer C is correct.**

   Many rear-wheel-drive sport utility vehicles and trucks use a load-sensing proportioning valve to modulate brake pressures in proportion to load. If the valve seizes in the loaded position and the load is removed, excess brake pressure will be applied to the rear brakes and cause lock-up.

101. **Answer B is correct.**

   A collapsed flex line can allow fluid flow to the caliper but not away from it. In this event, the right front-wheel brake will stay engaged until the fluid bleeds back through the collapsed line at a slow rate. Excess heat will be formed because the brakes will stay applied after the driver's foot has been removed from the pedal.

102. **Answer C is correct.**

   The thrust line is the angle relative to the centreline as determined by the total toe of the rear wheels. In short, the direction that the toe is pointing the rear wheels is essentially the direction the vehicle will want to travel in.

103. **Answer C is correct.**

   Brake shoes not resting on the anchor indicate that some application pressure has been applied. Of the possible answers, a seized parking brake is the most likely cause of brake shoes not retracting to the anchors.

104. **Answer B is correct.**

   A scratch cut is performed to make sure that the rotor is trued to the lathe arbor shaft. If the rotor is not true to the shaft, then the cut will be improper and lateral runout will occur when placed on the vehicle.

105. **Answer B is correct.**

   When testing a floating rotor for proper runout, it is important that any slack be taken up to ensure accurate readings. Torquing the wheel nuts to the rotor is the way to ensure that the rotor is tight to the hub assembly.

106. **Answer B is correct.**

   On the dynamometer, only the drive wheels spin. The anti-lock computer assumes that there is no speed output from the non-driven wheels and logs a diagnostic trouble code.

107. **Answer A is correct.**

Debris on the mounting flange such as dirt and rust can cause lateral runout. It is essential that the rotor and the hub flange be clean when mounting rotors.

108. **Answer C is correct.**

A low brake pedal can be caused by seized slider pins. If a floating caliper is unable to move, the lateral runout in the rotor (all rotors have some lateral runout) pushes back the caliper piston. The fluid is returned to the reservoir and the next brake application has to refill the caliper to take up the clearances.

109. **Answer C is correct.**

Traction control will be disabled in the event of an ABS malfunction because the two systems share some of the same components.

110. **Answer B is correct.**

The air dryer in an air brake system must be serviced regularly to ensure that clean and dry air is in the brake system. Moisture in the brake system is undesirable.

111. **Answer C is correct.**

Tire wear will be evident in the centre of the tire when the tire is over-inflated. The tire essentially balloons and rides solely in the centre of the tread.

112. **Answer C is correct.**

The wear indicator on this type of ball joint is the shoulder where the grease fitting attaches. When the shoulder recesses up into the body of the ball joint, the joint needs to be replaced.

113. **Answer B is correct.**

A seized strut bearing prevents the coil spring from rotating with the strut assembly. With a seized bearing, the coil spring will wind up, and if moved far enough, will snap or clunk the bearing to unload the spring slightly.

114. **Answer A is correct.**

The idler arm has slots built into the mounting component to allow for parallelism adjustments.

115. **Answer B is correct.**

A radial runout procedure measures the runout on both the tire and the rim. The tire tread needs to be measured radially. Measurements on the sidewall are lateral measurement.

116. **Answer A is correct.**

A dry park test must be conducted with the vehicle on level ground. The wheels must not be on a moveable or slippery surface. The purpose of the test is to check for wear at all moving steering components.

**117. Answer A is correct.**

A restricted pump inlet will cause fluid aeration because of the restriction and the low pressure.

**118. Answer C is correct.**

If the steering gear has improper preload, the steering gear is able to move outside of its normal range. This slop or slack in the gear can cause a wandering condition if too loose.

**119. Answer B is correct.**

Caster is measured by performing a caster sweep. Caster is not a live angle and after corrections, the caster sweep has to be made again to check the correction.


# Block G: Body Components, Trim, and Restraint Systems

**120. Answer A is correct.**

The air bag system requires that one sensor be active on both the positive and negative side of the deployment loop. Therefore 1 forward and 1 safing sensor must be closed for air bag deployment.

**121. Answer B is correct.**

The sensors must be installed so that they are at the correct angle and position for accuracy in determining a collision. Torquing the mounting bolts ensures that the sensor will not move in its mounted position.

**122. Answer B is correct.**

Since the motor is audibly working, the most likely cause is a broken window track where the window does not move (disconnected from the regulator) and the motor controls the regulator up and down without seeing the window move.

**123. Answer B is correct.**

Wind noise is usually caused by a piece of trim or other obstruction that interferes with the normal passage of air around the vehicle. Loose windscreen molding would cause such a noise.

**124. Answer A is correct.**

Many remote starter manufacturers include a grounding style hood pin switch to deactivate the system when the hood is open to prevent injury. If the hood wire is not shielded, it is possible to pick up magnetic pulses from the ignition system. The induction could trick the remote starter module into thinking the hood was open and cancel the start. This would not affect regular key operation.

**125. Answer D is correct.**

Most factory theft-deterrent systems use technology built into the key. This has evolved from a resistor pellet to a built-in radio frequency transmitter. To immobilize a vehicle, the system will usually shut off fuel to which the PCM has control. In this case, a defective key could cause the vehicle to initially start and then shut off because the wrong message, or no message, was received. Key readers are available and are usually dealer equipment.

# Explanations for Practice
# Test 3 Answers ➤ 11

## Block A: Occupational Skills

1. **Answer C is correct.**
   Class C extinguishers are suitable for use on electrically energized fires. The presence of the letter *C* indicates that the extinguishing agent is non-conductive.

2. **Answer C is correct.**
   Part of the worker's responsibility is to wear his or her proper personal protective equipment. However, the responsibility for ensuring that workers wear the proper protective equipment lies with the employer. For more information visit www.ccohs.ca.

3. **Answer D is correct.**
   For the most correct reading on a small-bore gauge, you should use an outside micrometer. Care should be taken not to disturb the reading on the small-bore gauge by using the ratcheting function on the micrometer.

4. **Answer B is correct.**
   A supplier label, under WHMIS regulations, must have the product identifier (name of product), supplier identifier (name of company that sold it), a statement that an MSDS is available, hazard symbols [the pictures of the classification(s)], risk phrases (words that describe the main hazards of the product), precautionary measures (how to work with the product safely), first aid measures (what to do in an emergency), have the WHMIS hatched border, and have all text in French and English.

5. **Answer B is correct.**
   Green valve caps indicate that the tire is inflated with nitrogen. There are no ill effects if a nitrogen-filled tire is topped up with plain old air. Nitrogen is said to keep tires 20% cooler and lengthen the life of the tire.

6. **Answer A is correct.**
   The 1st digit in the VIN indicates the country in which the vehicle was manufactured. For example: USA (1 or 4), Canada (2), Mexico (3), Japan (J), Korea (K), England (S), Germany (W), Italy (Z).

7. **Answer C is correct.**

Persistent and common problems found by vehicle manufacturers are published and sent to their dealer networks. These bulletins are called TSBs and contain useful information on vehicle diagnostic and repair procedures as well as new and improved parts and warranty and service manual updates.

8. **Answer B is correct.**

Released acetylene becomes unstable and explodes at pressures greater than 15 psi (103 kPa). It is imperative for acetylene to be used with a regulator. It is also recommended to have the regulator off when turning on the tank.

9. **Answer A is correct.**

According to most lift manufacturers, every shift should begin with a lift inspection. Your safety is paramount. In the United States, approximately 15,000 lift-related serious injuries are reported each year.

# Block B: Engine Systems

10. **Answer C is correct.**

If the vacuum valve portion of the radiator cap is open, there is always an open passageway between the radiator and the overflow bottle. The vacuum valve is designed to be closed under pressure and open when the radiator pressure drops below atmospheric or coolant overflow pressure. This would lead to lower system pressure and lower the boiling point of the coolant below design.

11. **Answer C is correct.**

The main spring of a thermostat controls system pressure. If the spring becomes weak or fails, the system will not be able to increase pressure. Remember that for every 1 psi of pressure on a contained system, it will increase the boiling point 3°F. This will result in a possible overheat condition and cause cylinder temperatures to increase. Increased cylinder temperatures will lead to pre-ignition.

12. **Answer A is correct.**

If the oil-pressure relief spring is weak, system pressure will not build as designed. It will relieve oil pressure too early and cause system pressure to be below specification. If the oil pump case clearance is out of specification by 0.002" (0.051 mm), it will not cause significant oil pressure problems.

13. **Answer C is correct.**

Wet compression tests are designed to take place after a dry compression test. If there is a suspect cylinder or cylinders, install about 15 ml of oil into the cylinder and perform the compression test again. If the cylinder pressure increases, investigation must go into the compression rings or cylinder wall.

14. **Answer C is correct.**
The refractometer is the most accurate for checking coolant strength. A refractometer does not measure specific gravity as a hydrometer does, but it measures concentration by the way light bends through it. This gives the most accurate measurement and is auto-temperature controlled. Also, it can handle both ethylene glycol and propylene glycol.

15. **Answer B is correct.**
The jiggle valve is designed to help bleed the cooling and prevent the formation of air pockets. The jiggle valve is normally placed in the UP position or at the top of the thermostat housing, since air will tend to rise.

16. **Answer D is correct.**
Coating the pump with assembly lube will protect the pump from oil starvation and damage when first started. The lube in the passageways will also help the pump gain its prime quickly.

17. **Answer B is correct.**
Plastigage™ is used to accurately measure various types of bearings. In this question, camshaft bearing clearance is the only answer that Plastigage™ would be capable of measuring accurately.

18. **Answer D is correct.**
Pressure is a direct result of restriction. In order to have excessive fuel pressure, there must be a restriction that will not allow fuel to flow, but rather build pressure against it. A restriction in the supply line would result in low fuel pressure to the injection system; therefore, a restriction in the return line will cause excessive fuel pressure.

19. **Answer C is correct.**
If an injector is open, it will not react when electrical current is supplied to it. If it cannot react, no fuel will be injected into that particular cylinder, resulting in a single cylinder misfire, even though the 2 or more injectors are commanded to inject together as a group.

20. **Answer A is correct.**
If an engine mount is broken, it will allow the engine to move off its mount in reaction to the engine, transmission, and driveline torque. Because engine mounts have a mechanical link that prevents them from separating, they will make a clunk noise as the two metallic pieces collide together.

21. **Answer C is correct.**
In order to test for a partially plugged catalytic converter, testing must occur upstream or before the catalytic converter. The easiest access to the exhaust pressure is through the oxygen sensor.

22. **Answer B is correct.**
Detonation occurs when combustion happens too slowly. Unburned air-fuel mixture ignites, not as part of the normal ignition process and the 2 flame fronts

collide. This results in a cylinder knock, and if left untreated can cause irreparable damage to the piston and/or cylinder.

23. **Answer D is correct.**
Piston ring flutter is a rapid oscillation of the piston ring in the ring land. Improper side clearance can cause this problem, resulting in a loss of cylinder compression and possible breakage of the ring.

24. **Answer C is correct.**
Air pumps are designed to inject air into the exhaust system to promote the oxidation process in the catalytic converter. Since the output of the air pump is directly connected to the exhaust system, a one-way check valve is used. This check valve, if defective, can allow hot exhaust gases into the air pump. This can lead to melting of plastic or composite components, thereby causing seizure and failure.

25. **Answer A is correct.**
During a cylinder leakage test, if there is more than 20% leakage, this is considered poor. If air is heard escaping from the oil fill, the air that has been injected into the combustion chamber is escaping to the crankcase. The route from the combustion chamber to the crankcase is through the piston rings.

26. **Answer B is correct.**
Torque plates are plates that bolt onto the cylinder deck to mimic the stresses that the cylinder head will place on the cylinder when it is properly torqued. If machining is done without torque plates, cylinders can be machined out of round. Using the plates will allow for truer machining, less distortion, and a better overall fit.

27. **Answer C is correct.**
All of the answers in this question could lead to cylinder block cracking. With technology today, metallurgical failures do not occur as often. Collisions do occur. The most common cause of block cracking, however, is an engine overheating condition.

## Block C: Vehicle Management Systems

28. **Answer B is correct.**
Advanced ignition timing is a common cause of a warm engine, "hard to start" complaint on an engine that starts easily when cold.

29. **Answer C is correct.**
A vacuum leak is a common cause of a low $O_2$ sensor output reading. The result is interpreted by the engine controller as a lean burn condition, and it accordingly overfuels the engine.

30. **Answer B is correct.**

ECT and IAT should produce equal readings after a prolonged shutdown period. Learn the common OBD II acronyms and the roles they play.

31. **Answer C is correct.**

There are 16 pins in an OBD II-compliant data link connector.

32. **Answer B is correct.**

The minimum number of data freeze-frames captured by an OBD II-compliant vehicle when the PCM logs a DTC is 1. However, most current systems are capable of logging a greater number of freeze-frames, although a proprietary scan tool may be required to access them.

33. **Answer C is correct.**

All OBD II Type A and B diagnostic trouble codes relate directly or indirectly to the emission control system. Most current vehicles use SAE J1850 data bus (multiplexing) protocols, but OEMs are only required to make OBD II conditions readable on generic scan tools: a J1850 data bus is capable of displaying detailed data on all the vehicle computer-control circuits, but in most cases proprietary PC software or scan tools are required to read this data.

34. **Answer B is correct.**

A standard 16-pin, OBD II-compliant data link connector dedicates pin #4 for chassis ground. You should learn the pin assignments for Bus +, Bus –, chassis ground, and signal ground: note that Bus – usually carries some voltage potential.

35. **Answer D is correct.**

A *warm-up cycle* is defined for purposes of OBD II code status as an event in which the engine coolant temperature increases by at least 22°C (71.6°F) and in doing so, exceeds 70°C (155°F). For instance, an MIL will deactivate after the PCM monitors 3 consecutive warm-up cycles through which a DTC is not detected. Once the MIL has been deactivated, the DTC will be logged in memory for a further 40 warm-up cycles before it is erased.

36. **Answer C is correct.**

If a coolant temperature sensor terminal is unplugged from the coolant sensor on a warm engine, the result is to log a DTC indicating an open (voltage low) and the displayed scan tool reading will usually be at the minimum value.

37. **Answer D is correct.**

A low output voltage from a standard $O_2$ sensor suggests a lean condition. There are 2 causes of a "false" lean condition: one is a dead cylinder, meaning that unreacted oxygen is dumped into the exhaust; and the other is air being pulled into the exhaust system, so a cracked exhaust manifold is a likely cause. The other conditions are more likely to result in a higher $O_2$ voltage.

38. **Answer D is correct.**
Depending on the specific engine and fuel system, the range of air-fuel ratios runs from about 8:1 up to 17:1. Generally, a leaner mixture is required for normal cruising and light load operation, while a richer than stoichiometric mixture is required for idling, heavy load, and hard acceleration. Make sure you know how to define *stoichiometric*.

39. **Answer B is correct.**
Changing to a higher octane fuel is the only answer that makes sense. Many fuels sold today are cut with ethanol: ethanols usually have a higher octane rating than gasoline but in the question stem, the octane rating is specified. Ping or knock is caused by too rapid combustion of the fuel; it can be remedied by increasing the octane rating or retarding ignition timing.

40. **Answer B is correct.**
The fuel rail pressure should increase when the vacuum hose is removed from the regulator. When system vacuum drops off as when the throttle is fully opened, the regulator responds by stepping up rail pressure. Make sure you understand how a fuel regulator operates: this is a common source of AST C of Q questions.

41. **Answer D is correct.**
A noid (short for solenoid) light test is used to diagnose fuel injector circuit malfunctions: the fuel injector is disconnected and the noid light placed in the circuit. The noid light should illuminate in sequence when the engine is run. A noid light that illuminates but appears to be dim suggests high resistance in the fuel injector wiring circuit: it cannot suggest an injector coil problem because to insert the noid light into the circuit, the fuel injector has to be disconnected.

42. **Answer A is correct.**
A restricted fuel filter may cause a rise in fuel pressure, slowing and overloading the fuel pump in some OEM models. You can verify the problem by checking fuel flow volume downstream from the filter. Note that one OEM had a problem with fuel pump whine in the 1990s that is not associated with reduced flow.

43. **Answer C is correct.**
In this situation, you should recommend that all 6 fuel injectors be replaced given the mileage on the vehicle, fuel balance considerations, and the fact that purchasing a full set of injectors is more economical than purchasing them in smaller numbers. Note that gasoline fuel injectors are seldom repaired in the field; they are removed and replaced by the technician.

44. **Answer C is correct.**
When fuel drips from the vacuum hose that connects to a vacuum-modulated fuel pressure regulator when it is disconnected, the cause is usually a failed regulator diaphragm.

45. **Answer A is correct.**

When scoping a pulse width-actuated injector, the inductive kick (spike) occurs when the injector coil is de-energized and its magnetic field collapses. It should therefore occur at the end of the pulse width on the display graphic.

46. **Answer D is correct.**

The inductive kick displayed in a scope graphic of injector pulse width will be observed to gradually reduce in length as the engine warms to operating temperature because the coil is energized for a shorter period when the engine is at operating temperature. Note also that pulse width real-time duration will also reduce.

47. **Answer C is correct.**

If the oxidizing stage of a catalytic converter on a gasoline engine is functioning properly, the exhaust gas temperature at the converter outlet should be greater than that at the inlet because in essence, unburned HC and CO are being combusted in the converter. The differential should be around 15% once the engine is at operating temperature and under normal loads, but there are many variables here.

48. **Answer A is correct.**

A coil-on-plug ignition system eliminates spark plug wires. This is one of the more common ignition systems today.

49. **Answer C is correct.**

The shield used on an optical ignition sensor must be lightproof. If this is left off, the result will be rough engine operation.

50. **Answer B is correct.**

A defective high-tension wire almost always destroys the coil that fires it. The high voltage produced by the coil, deprived of its intended ground path, arcs within the coil, creating a short circuit to the primary windings known as a carbon track.

51. **Answer A is correct.**

A transistor switches primary circuit current in the ignition module in a typical electronic ignition circuit. Transistors are solid-state components that act like an electronic relay switch: they allow the ignition module to signal the primary transistor with a low-potential voltage.

52. **Answer B is correct.**

When platinum spark plugs are to be reused, the threads should be lightly coated with never-seize compound (because they require so little service attention and are more likely to seize) and no attempt should be made to regap them. If the gap is well outside specification, replace them.

53. **Answer A is correct.**

When scoping a good pair of plugs on a waste spark ignition system, the power spark is distinguished from the waste spark on an oscilloscope display by a higher firing line. This is caused by increased cylinder pressure, meaning that the voltage required to maintain the spark is increased.

## 54. **Answer D is correct.**

When you disconnect a high-tension wire on a running engine during troubleshooting, you must ground the wire. Failure to do so can destroy the ignition coil (see the explanation for question #50 of this test).

# Block D: Drive Line Systems

## 55. **Answer B is correct.**

If a universal joint has more than 1/8" (3.18 mm) play, you would be able to feel it by grasping both halves; however, to properly check a universal joint, you must remove the driveshaft and check for roughness in the joint by moving it around. The joint should feel smooth and not bind in any direction.

## 56. **Answer C is correct.**

On hard acceleration, if the leaf springs are weak, axle wind-up can occur. This will change the operating angle of the driveshaft's rear universal joint resulting in an acceleration shudder. Under normal acceleration, this may not be felt. It would depend on the weakness of the leaf spring.

## 57. **Answer A is correct.**

When the clutch is disengaged (foot is on clutch pedal) the input shaft of the transmission is spinning at a different speed to the flywheel because there is no engagement of the clutch. This results in the input shaft spinning in the pilot bearing. When the clutch is engaged, the input shaft and the flywheel turn at the same speed, thereby eliminating the noise.

## 58. **Answer A is correct.**

If the O-ring on a transmission filter were to fail, it is possible for air to be drawn into the pump as well as some fluid. This could cause fluid aeration. Since air is compressible, shifting pressure will be lower and therefore cause slipping.

## 59. **Answer B is correct.**

Bench testing a clutch pack or servo on the bench should be done with a rubber-tipped air nozzle. This will air-test the unit, and if air is heard escaping or action is not achieved, the unit is faulty.

## 60. **Answer D is correct.**

If the stator in a torque converter hangs up and remains locked, at high speed the torque converter will work against itself. The vehicle may drive normally while accelerating at low speed but will cause engine strain at higher speeds. Therefore, performance at higher speeds will be reduced.

## 61. **Answer A is correct.**

If the clutch pedal free play is too great, when the clutch is fully depressed the clutch will not be fully disengaged. If the clutch is not fully disengaged, the input shaft will not be disengaged from the flywheel. If this occurs, shifting will not be smooth because the engine and transmission will never disengage.

62. **Answer C is correct.**

On a gear-to-gear transfer case, a manual transmission-style synchronizer sleeve connects the two components. If the transfer case will not uncouple, it is likely that the shift collar is binding and not allowing the two shafts to spin independently.

63. **Answer A is correct.**

If backlash in a differential is too great, the tooth pattern when tested will be close to the heel. Correction is needed for proper differential operation and longevity.

64. **Answer C is correct.**

After changing a worn transmission mount, the driveline angles should be checked to ensure that the proper angle is achieved. Possibilities exist to shim the new mount or rear end to make sure driveline angles are correct for smooth and proper operation.

65. **Answer D is correct.**

If the lubricant is not correct in a transmission, it is possible for all shifts to be harsh and crunchy. Some transmissions use different compounds on the synchronizer blocking rings. With these compounds, they must be filled with the correct fluid so the transmissions will shift properly. Always use manufacturer-specified transmission fluid when changing or topping-up manual transmission fluid.

66. **Answer C is correct.**

When transmission fluid becomes hot, the solenoids that the fluid passes through do as well. If a pressure control solenoid has an electrical failure, it is possible for the heat to change the resistance in the coil. If this happens, the electrical signal from the transmission controller will not change the pressure as needed. If this happens and the shift slips, after a specified number of slipping shifts the transmission controller will default to main line pressure. This will cause harsh shifting until the problem is corrected.

67. **Answer C is correct.**

If an automatic transmission shift linkage is out of adjustment, it is possible for the entire transmission manual range not to be achieved. All bushings and springs on a transmission linkage must be intact and lubricated for proper operation.

68. **Answer A is correct.**

The throttle position sensor is an input for an electronic transmission. If the throttle position sensor malfunctions and does not supply a signal, it is possible for the transmission not to shift because it does not recognize throttle input.

69. **Answer C is correct.**

Torsion springs on a clutch disk are designed to absorb harsh clutch applications. If the torsion springs are weak and broken, this could lead to harsh clutch applications.

70. **Answer D is correct.**

If the 4th-gear shaft is worn, the clutch pack cannot be held. This would lead to a command from the PCM but no transmission reaction. The solenoids would react to the signal and the slipping shaft would not permit 4th gear to lock in.

71. **Answer A is correct.**

When servicing 4x4 locking hubs, they should be clean and lightly lubricated to ensure smooth and bind-free operation.

72. **Answer C is correct.**

A worn tailshaft bushing could cause the output shaft seal to leak. This would cause the driveshaft to wobble and be unable to obtain a tight seal.

# Block E: Electrical and Comfort Control Systems

73. **Answer B is correct.**

An ammeter capable of accurately reading milliamps must be used. The preferred method of performing the test is to use an inductive pickup digital ammeter clamped onto the positive cable close to the battery-positive terminal. An older method would be to use an ammeter placed in series between a separated positive battery terminal and post.

74. **Answer C is correct.**

The ignition-off current draw required by current vehicles with multiple control modules networked to a chassis data bus can be up to 0.060 amps. When performing the IOD test, ensure that the vehicle ignition has been switched off for at least 20 minutes. This will ensure that all of the computers are in "sleep" mode.

75. **Answer C is correct.**

When the insulation on a 12V-DC wire fails and it contacts the chassis, a short to ground has occurred. A fire should not occur unless the circuit protection device has been bypassed.

76. **Answer A is correct.**

An additional electrical accessory spliced into the insulated circuit provides another path for current flow. Voltage applied to the circuit would remain the same, while total circuit resistance would drop (due to the added path).

77. **Answer C is correct.**

The preferred method of testing the integrity of a series of standard blade-type fuses in an electrical fuse panel is to use a DVOM in V-DC mode and test each fuse in position at shoulder test points, because this method does not require the removal of the fuse from the circuit. Caution: use the DVOM in V-DC mode and test each fuse in position at shoulder test points with circuits energized!

78. **Answer A is correct.**

AWG (American Wire Gauge) cable sectional areas increase in size as the number specification lowers. The electrical cable sizes suitable for automobile battery cables are AWG numbers 0, 1, 2, and 4. Note that AWG sizes descend below zero, as in 00, 000, and 0000, with the last having the highest sectional area and therefore having the highest current-carrying capability.

79. **Answer B is correct.**
The colour used for the high-voltage wiring insulation in high-potential hybrid vehicle electrical circuits (144V, 275V, 432V) is orange: extreme caution should be exercised when working around high-potential circuits.

80. **Answer D is correct.**
As a rule in electrical circuit troubleshooting, it makes sense to begin by checking out the relay. The relay is usually easy to access and will provide an immediate indication of whether the problem is in the control or power circuit of the malfunctioning component.

81. **Answer C is correct.**
When a battery has to be disconnected from a vehicle, a 12V-DC memory saver should be plugged into a power outlet/lighter socket to ensure no memory loss occurs to any of the vehicle computers networked to the data bus. This is simply good customer service. The consequences of not protecting on-board memory will require the rewriting of power control module running strategies (may take up to 80 km of operation) and resetting of radio presets.

82. **Answer D is correct.**
When the high-voltage battery pack becomes discharged on a hybrid-drive vehicle, the primary (high-voltage) starter will not crank the engine. However, most hybrid vehicles are equipped with a secondary 12V-DC starter motor to cover this situation. Never attempt any type of high-voltage boost under these circumstances—it can be dangerous.

83. **Answer C is correct.**
This is a standard test on one type of commonly used alternator. A DVOM is used in ohmmeter mode and although it can be performed in-vehicle, the battery must be disconnected before the test is performed.

84. **Answer D is correct.**
The DRL on some manufacturers' vehicles are designed to switch off when the parking brake is actuated; this acts as a power saver when the vehicle is being serviced.

85. **Answer C is correct.**
A feedback connection at the bulb circuit between the turn and tail-light terminals could cause this condition. The increased flashing is a result of higher current load through the flasher circuit.

86. **Answer B is correct.**
The stoplight switch usually supplies an input signal to the cruise-control electronics that is used to interrupt set speed programming.

87. **Answer D is correct.**
HID light units are illuminated by electrical discharge fired between two electrodes encased in a xenon gas-filled tube. A very high-potential arc is created to ignite the arc, after which a potential of around 80 volts is required to maintain it. Used properly, HID lights last much longer than any current type of incandescent lights: the main cause of failure is burned electrodes resulting from frequent short on/off cycles or headlight flashing.

88. **Answer D is correct.**
A voltage loss of 0.8 V on the insulated side of a headlight is unacceptable. Make sure you know how to perform voltage-drop testing on some of the typical specifications you might expect to see.

89. **Answer D is correct.**
Virtual circuit breakers are becoming more commonly used, and they differ from mechanical circuit breakers in that there are no moving parts: they are solid state and cycle on and off, controlled by microprocessor signal.

90. **Answer B is correct.**
The common terminal is coded #3 (this was coded #30 using the older terminal allocations). Make sure you can correlate the new and older terminal assignments; this can be invaluable in troubleshooting.

91. **Answer C is correct.**
Two wires are used in the multiplexing backbone used by a CAN 2.0 data bus (J1850): specifically this is a twisted wire pair that may or may not be shielded. This forms the data backbone of a vehicle multiplex communications system.

92. **Answer A is correct.**
When troubleshooting any complaint, eliminate the easy potential causes of the problem first. In the case of insufficient passenger compartment heat during cold weather operation, you should check the temperature of the upper radiator hose when the engine appears to be at operating temperature first. This requires the least amount of time and will indicate how the coolant is being circulated in the system and the role played by the thermostat.

93. **Answer C is correct.**
The more costly consequence of using mineral base oil in an HFC-134a A/C system would be its potential to cause a compressor failure due to lack of lubrication. HFC-134a systems must use PAG or esther-based refrigerants. Using the mineral base oil in an HFC-134a system will contaminate the refrigerant and may also cause system underperformance, but neither will be as costly as a compressor replacement.

94. **Answer A is correct.**
The circuit for the field coils of an A/C compressor clutch should be tested for voltage using a voltmeter: when activated, there should be battery or system voltage present.

95. **Answer A is correct.**
The only time that both the high- and low-side hand valves on an A/C system should be open at the same time is during evacuation or reclaiming refrigerant with the system not running.

96. **Answer D is correct.**
If an HFC-134a A/C system were to be 25% overcharged with refrigerant during servicing it would operate at lower efficiency than specified. Always use the specified weight of refrigerant.

97. **Answer B is correct.**
The failsafe device used in an HFC-134a AC system in the event of a high-pressure service valve leak is an O-ring located in the service valve cap. You should check the integrity of this O-ring each time the A/C system is serviced.

# Block F: Steering, Suspension, Braking, and Control Systems

98. **Answer C is correct.**
A dry park test is designed to test steering linkages by putting road forces on the steering linkages. Steering linkage play is visible and able to be felt when the steering wheel is turned back and forth with the wheels on the ground with vehicle weight on them.

99. **Answer B is correct.**
When working on an air bag system, you need to be aware that the diagnostic module contains capacitors to allow for air bag deployment with the battery disconnected. This means that before performing any work you should disconnect the battery and wait a few minutes for the capacitors to discharge.

100. **Answer C is correct.**
While performing a worm-bearing preload adjustment, a spring scale is necessary to make sure that the steering effort is not too great or too little at the wheel. If the effort is too great, the worm-bearing preload must be lessened, and if the effort is too little, the preload must be increased. This will prolong steering box life and allow for comfortable driver steering effort.

101. **Answer B is correct.**
If the height sensor wiring has high resistance, the control module for the air ride suspension will not signal an air increase to the rear air springs. The height sensor sends feedback to the module on the rear ride height. If the signal is incorrect, the module will not trigger the compressor to increase ride height.

102. **Answer A is correct.**
Strut bearings are in place so that the spring will rotate with the strut and not try to coil up as the wheel turns. The bearing is load-bearing, and if it becomes dry or worn, it will tend to make noise as it rotates through normal steering. If it becomes significantly worse, it will tend to seize and snap through steering.

103. **Answer C is correct.**

The subframe connects the engine and drivetrain to the body on most unibody-designed vehicles. For vibration reasons, the subframe is attached using long bolts and rubber mounts. As the mounts wear, the torque from the drivetrain can cause the subframe to shift and clunk. Heavy deceleration can also cause the subframe to shift.

104. **Answer C is correct.**

Any time space has to be taken up in a hydraulic system, pedal movement will increase. Although a seized star wheel will not allow rear brake shoes to self-adjust, the amount of clearance between drum and shoe is not known. Excessive rotor runout will knock the piston in the caliper back further than it should. The further the piston is back in the bore, the more fluid needs to be displaced to push the piston out until clamping force can occur.

105. **Answer D is correct.**

In a vacuum booster, the poppet valve controls the atmospheric and vacuum ports. If the valve is leaking from the vacuum portion, atmospheric pressure will be allowed to flow into both halves of the booster. With equal pressures on both halves of the diaphragm, no power assist will be present, resulting in a hard pedal.

106. **Answer C is correct.**

Brake fluid found on the floor in the vehicle is caused by a leaking master cylinder. The secondary seal on the primary piston in the master allows fluid to leak into the vacuum booster. If enough fluid accumulates in the booster, some can leak out the atmospheric port and onto the carpet.

107. **Answer D is correct.**

Sealed wheel bearings generally make noise when the bearing is loaded. A left front-wheel bearing is loaded the most when turning right and decelerating because of body roll and pitch.

108. **Answer A is correct.**

Scalloping of the tire occurs when the tire bounces on the road. The purpose of the shock absorbers is to dampen spring oscillations and keep the tires on the ground.

109. **Answer C is correct.**

Replacing a pitman arm can sometimes be a difficult task because the steering gear shaft is tapered. This creates a wedge fit, and after a number of years can be difficult to dislodge with pullers and pickle forks. Many technicians use heat on a pitman arm but find that after the pitman arm is replaced, a power steering leak occurs. This is due to the heat melting the output shaft seal.

110. **Answer A is correct.**

The shut-off valve needs to be closed to check the power steering pump output. When the valve is closed, compare the reading with the manufacturer's specifications. Note that the valve should not be closed for more than 5 seconds as damage will occur to the power steering pump from overheated fluid.

111. **Answer C is correct.**

Most systems that have a strut bar use the strut bar to adjust caster. Adjusting the strut bar will change the position of the lower control arm and ball joint.

112. **Answer D is correct.**

On a 4-wheel alignment, the first adjustment to be made is rear camber. After rear camber, rear toe should be adjusted and then adjust the front angles.

113. **Answer A is correct.**

If the vehicle and frame centrelines do not match up from subframe misalignment, SAI and camber angles will not be equal from side to side. The included angle is the addition of SAI and camber. If the included angles are equal but the readings are out of specification, check the alignment of the subframe.

114. **Answer B is correct.**

If there is a large clearance between the caliper and the knuckle where the caliper mounts, with brake application the caliper will grab the rotor, and due to the large clearance, pull it around and peen the knuckle. Clearance on some brake systems can be taken up with shims or increased by filing.

115. **Answer D is correct.**

The pressure differential valve compares the brake pressures between each circuit. If there is a failure in the hydraulic system (the leaking wheel cylinder) the pressures will be unequal and cause the switch to close and illuminate the red brake-warning lamp. Some pressure differential valves require resetting after they have been tripped. This would require the removal of the switch, re-centre the valve and re-install the switch.

116. **Answer B is correct.**

Metering valves are designed to delay the application of the front brakes until the rear brakes have started to generate some braking force. This is to provide better braking balance. The metering valve is open until 5–30 psi (34.5–206.8 kPa) and then closes until around 100 psi (689.5 kPa). A pressure bleeder forces fluid through the system. If the setting on the pressure bleeder is too high, it will close the metering valve, stopping the flow of fluid to the front brakes.

117. **Answer A is correct.**

An erratic wheel speed code is usually generated because of an intermittent connection. Likely causes are connector pin tension as well as loose connections in the coil of the wheel speed sensor. If an erratic code is generated, focus on the connections at the affected wheel.

118. **Answer C is correct.**

The most accurate place to take wheel runout measurements is on the inside of the rim with the tire removed. Curb damage and dirt can affect measurements taken on the outside of the rim.

119. **Answer D is correct.**

When only one end of the roller has scoring, it is usually caused by excessive preload. This is because the excessive pressure loads on the large end of the tapered roller element. The bearing is too tight and is heating up rapidly while working.

## Block G: Body Components, Trim, and Restraint Systems

120. **Answer A is correct.**

Most supplemental restraint system sensors have arrows on them to ensure proper installation. Arrows must point to the front of the vehicle in order for proper system operation in the event of a collision.

121. **Answer C is correct.**

On a parallelogram-type of steering system that uses a tie rod sleeve, the sleeve is split. If it is positioned incorrectly, the air rushing past it while driving can act like a flute. Slight rotation of the sleeve to keep the split out of the wind path will solve this problem.

122. **Answer B is correct.**

The most effective way to trace water and wind leaks in a vehicle is to use a smoke machine. Smoke fills the vehicle and the technician is able to see the escape path. Electronic stethoscopes and tone generators can also be used if available.

123. **Answer C is correct.**

The only ground on most power window systems is located at the master switch in the driver's door. If all windows become inoperative, check the wiring diagram and find the ground-point connection.

124. **Answer D is correct.**

Before making any adjustments to a door hinge, you must check to see that the hinge is not the cause of the sag. Lifting up on the door and checking for play is an effective way to check the hinges on the door. Hinges are to be replaced, not repaired.

125. **Answer C is correct.**

Because the doors swing open and closed repeatedly, making wiring repairs in the door jamb is not effective. In the event of a broken wire, you should pull a new wire through and make the solder connections in areas where there is no excessive wire movement.

# Recommended Study Texts ➤ 12

---

The following textbooks can be used as guides to Canadian AST C of Q tests. They are used in the colleges that prepare apprentices for the in-school requirements of apprenticeship. Most are available in college bookstores or the online retail services of national retailers. Some of the books are specialty books dealing in depth with the subject matter they address, while others are general in nature. A brief description follows each book.

### Automotive Technology: A Systems Approach, 4th Edition
Author:      Jack Erjavec
ISBN:      1-4018-4831-1
Publisher:      Delmar ITC, New York
Review:      Covers all automotive systems. A large, comprehensive textbook with plenty of detail and anecdotal troubleshooting/repair content.

### Automotive Technology—Canadian Edition
Author:      James Halderman with Mitchell, Marchant, and Davey
ISBN:      0-13124890-1
Publisher:      Prentice Hall, New Jersey
Review:      Excellent introduction to auto electricity and electronics and covers the chassis bumper-to-bumper with down-to-earth explanations.

### Automotive Encyclopedia
Author:      Toboldt, Olive and Johnson
ISBN:      0-8700-6691-9
Publisher:      Goodheart Wilcox
Review:      Covers all automotive systems comprehensively.

### Automotive Service
Author:      Tim Gilles
ISBN:      0-8273-7354-6
Publisher:      Delmar ITC, New York
Review:      Covers all automotive systems in simple, easy-to-understand language.

### Bosch Automotive Handbook

ISBN:         (none)
Publisher:    Bosch GmbH/SAE
Review:      Technically detailed text. Some of the content pertains only to European practices.

### Dictionary of Automotive Technology

Author:      Sean Bennett
ISBN:         0-919852-37-8
Publisher:    Centennial College Press, Toronto
Review:      Simple explanation of automotive terms. Especially good for ESL (English as a second language) students.

### Today's Technician Series

Author:      Various
ISBN:         Various
Review:      Series of books dealing with AST certification by the (National Institute for) Automotive Service Excellence (ASE) in the US, each one specializing in a different automotive system. Can be useful study guides, especially if you have a weakness in one study area, but the question structure addresses ASE tests with lots of Tech A/Tech B questions.

# Notes

# Notes

# Notes

# Notes

# Notes

# Notes

# Notes

# Notes